# CIRCLE TIME

Third Anthology
of Poetry and Prose from
Dalkey Writers' Workshop

foreword by
Joseph O'Connor

edited by
Paul Perry

# Acknowledgements

Dalkey Writers' Workshop wishes to thank the following people for their contribution to this publication:

Joseph O'Connor for his foreword,
Paul Perry for his editing,
Jill Arthur for her proofreading,
Billy Hutchinson for handling the design & print production,
The members of Dalkey Writers' Workshop.

Anthology Committee:
Joe McNally, Eileen Counihan, Madeline Stringer.

Sponsorship:
The Club, 107 Coliemore Road, Dalkey.
Tesco Ireland.

The production of this anthology has been supported by
Dún Laoghaire-Rathdown County Council Arts Office:

Comhairle Contae County Council

First edition
Published by Dalkey Writers' Workshop, 2011
dalkeywritersworkshop.wordpress.com

© Copyright remains with the authors

ISBN 978-0-9551422-2-2

Cover and page design by:    4D Design,
                             Tel: 086-833-5094,
                             billy@4DdesignDublin.com

Fonts:    Main body text:    11.3pt Garamond
          Titles:            13pt Trajan Pro

Printed in Ireland by:       Gemini International, Damastown, Dublin 15

# FOREWORD

In his poem 'The Given Note', Seamus Heaney describes an old Irish traditional air coasting out of the atmosphere 'on loud weather'. There's been plenty of loudness in Ireland recently. We're living through days of fury. Yet the work of storytellers and poets, of memoirists and musicians, has been finding a way up through the swamp of recession, just as punk did in its time and place, and rap, and gospel, as the blues bubbled up from the Mississippi. The wrecked Dublin of my adolescence was re-energised not by any politician, but by the explosion of music and related creativities that was detonated in the late 1970s. The feeling was that in the act of creativity remarkable enrichments can happen. That's the energy behind this book.

Ireland faces immense challenges. Old certainties are broken. But one treasure we continue to have is the extraordinary resource of the written word. And when all the swarming lies around us are dust and old headlines, we'll still have it. It's then we're going to need it the most.

More of us than ever before have been coming back to the written word: in writers' groups, in book clubs, through the internet, in the workplace. It's as though we wish to return to some of the better values of the past – respect for the act of storytelling, the importance of expression – while simultaneously coming to a realisation that the carving out of a better future will mean we must empower ourselves to say what we're thinking.

For some writers, both published and coming to writing for the first time, a sense of place has been remarkably central. Many of the writers included in the present collection are neighbours, residents of a fascinating district. Like all villages anywhere, Dalkey has its ways, its cliques, factions, sets and elites, and some of the pieces included in this collection establish a vivid sense of the multiplicity of the place. Myths are overturned, easy caricatures subverted, and there is a nicely implied sense, as in Dylan Thomas's Under Milk

Joseph O'Connor

# FOREWORD

Wood, or Thornton Wilder's Our Town, that while the clichés of any community have become clichés for a reason, life is not quite as it seems.

Part country-style village, part rapidly changing suburb, for some years Dalkey's very name has served as a lazy social shorthand, and while it is true that some of Ireland's wealthiest live in the area, so do many other people, of many kinds. There is a much older and invariably more fascinating Dalkey, still observable in the daily trawler life of Bullock Harbour's fishermen, and in Cuala, one of the largest GAA clubs in the country, and in the beautiful squares of old Corporation houses that adjoin one of the earliest thoroughfares in Ireland, Castle Street. And if you asked the late Hugh Leonard if the Dalkey of his boyhood was a realm of high living, I feel certain his reply would have been as stylishly acerbic as was his polished and beautiful writing.

The town has long had a nexus of literary and political associations. Shaw and Casement lived nearby, as did Joyce, Synge, and Gogarty. Indeed, a central chapter of Joyce's Ulysses is set in a schoolhouse on Dalkey Avenue. Flann O'Brien's masterpiece The Dalkey Archive imagined the then sleepy little backwater as the setting for linguistic shenanigans and cosmological farce, while that peerless storyteller and local heroine Maeve Binchy still lives in the village of her girlhood. The presence of Bono, The Edge and Van Morrisson in the neighbourhood means the occasional celebrity is spotted, but generally they go undisturbed. The touch of rock and roll glamour has not altered the character of a place that is essentially an Irish seaside village, very pretty when dressed up, full of eccentricities and myths, but not without a little grit under its fingernails.

There are pubs in the town which are frequented by the bored and the beautiful, and where Ross O'Carroll-Kelly himself might find it, loik, quoysh hord to get in, but the less easily wowed will

Joseph O'Connor

# FOREWORD

notice the quieter little places where the townspeople of an older era quietly socialize as they have done for many decades. And all residents, tourists and other visitors will know that the proximity of the sea and of the coastal glories of Killiney and Dun Laoghaire give that whole stretch of shoreline a storm-blown beauty that throws sand in the eyes but raises fire in the heart. The first girl I ever fell in love with was a native of Dalkey, and to trudge Dalkey Island in a November gale brings her still, to this day, to my mind. Thirty years later we are still warm friends, and I intend sending her and her family a copy of this tender-hearted book. Forget the lazy assumptions and tired journalistic shorthand. Dalkey, behind it all, is a special and precious place, and this charming collection of writings is testament to the fact that our neighbourhood is still producing plenty of storytellers.

A story, like a song, takes its chances alone. It needs the reader to bring it to life. What the reader does is the truly creative part of the relationship, for in the unique and intimate courtship opened out by the book, the little black ink-stains called 'words' and 'sentences' are blazed into life by imagination. And this anthology, a great meeting of readers and writers, speaks to those of us who have been thrilled and changed by a story, and who need to be so uplifted again. Here is a collection of writers with something meaningful to say, their words finding breath on the air. I warmly congratulate everyone involved in this project, and I think every reader will find something touching within these pages.

Joseph O'Connor
Dublin, 2011

# Contents

# CONTENTS

# The Atmospheric Railway

Amidst all the wonders afforded the modern world, there is none to compare to the miracle of mechanical transportation. I remember the day I first saw a steam locomotive. My father was a professor at Trinity College, a gentleman and a gentle educator, who believed a child, could not learn by force and harshness, but could be lead to learning if directed to what amused his mind.

It was the last day of term and my father was bringing me to his office as a special treat. He took me by the hand that summer morning, beneath the gaze of the great houses of Merrion Square, and into Westland Row, where the new railway bridge stretched above the dust dry street. Horse drawn carriages rattled past, and children ran playfully this way and that amid the coarse cries of the jarvies.

As we approached the bridge a small boy, barefoot and untidy, stretched his arms above his head and pointed excitedly. His friends quickly joined him, shouting with glee, and a small girl ran into a doorway where she crouched like a frightened mouse. Wild-eyed horses strained at the bit as a sudden rush of white steam escaped the station roof.

And then it came, huffing and puffing and panting. A giant of iron and steel glistened above us, and belched fire from its cast iron belly.

'There she is!' shouted my father above the noise. 'Hibernian!'

The engineer pulled a chain with his rag covered hand, and her whistle hooted and tooted. I could see the coal man stoking her fire, and steam hissed as pistons pushed, and she pulled and tugged the wood and steel wagons strapped to her back. I watched her wheels slip and grip as she struggled and rattled and chugged her way across the bridge and out of sight with her brass bell tolling.

Then all was quiet, and all I could hear was my heart thump thumping in my chest. And all I could feel was my hand in his.

'A masterpiece of the mind' my father called her, and at that

# THE ATMOSPHERIC RAILWAY

moment I could see her creator with rule in hand, bent over drawings and calculations, and I knew what I wanted to do with my life.

I followed my father to Trinity.

A first year student of engineering, young, brash and impatient, I felt shackled by my own youth. There was a well within me, which I needed to fill with mathematical equations and engineering formulae. The more I studied the more I could feel this learning surge inside me. I longed for this well to become a fountain and release. I feared Isambard Kingdom Brunel, the little genius, would not leave a river to cross, or a single track for me to lay in the whole of the empire. I envied and admired him in equal measure.

The Dublin to Kingstown railway was by now a great success, and work was almost complete on its extension to Dalkey. However, the enthusiasm I held for the railway, and for all things modern and inventive, was not shared by everyone. Farmers feared the noisy and dirty engines would frighten their cattle and pollute their crops. Many in the cities added that sparks could ignite terrible fires, the like of which had once destroyed London town. I poured scorn on these nay-sayers, but greater minds than mine had offered a solution.

The Atmospheric Railway, as it was to be known, would not only be silent and clean, but could climb a hill more efficiently than any steam locomotive. It came as no surprise to me that the Atmospheric Railway was championed by the great Brunel himself.

The principle was ingeniously simple. A cast iron pipe ran between the tracks, in which a piston was forced to run by pressure of air. The piston was attached to the carriage above, and so pulled it along the length of the pipe.

Through my father's good office, I managed to secure a junior position for myself as an assistant to one of the assistant engineers. I

# THE ATMOSPHERIC RAILWAY

remember how my father laughed when I explained just how junior my position was.

"The pipe must be open at the top to allow the carriage to be connected to the piston," I explained.

"In that case how do you prevent loss of compression?" he enquired.

"Leather flaps are overlaid and greased with liberal quantities of wax and tallow," I explained. "The solution has not yet been perfected, as rats are attracted to the tallow, and are gnawing their way through the leather. My duty is to walk the line and grease the pipe."

"The pied piper of Dalkey" he quipped. "I always said you would achieve something of note."

"We are working on a solution, Father."

"I have heard it said," he continued, "that the train will not make the climb to Dalkey, and that if it falls short of the station, the unfortunate passengers will be expected to disembark and push!"

"Only those in 3rd class, Father."

As the line approached completion, testing became more rigorous, the working day became stretched, and tempers more likely to fray.

The site foreman was a brute of a man, a hard life and hard living had made him so. The evidence was etched in his face. He wore an old fustian jacket and a greasy cap pulled tightly over his head. I don't think he or any of his navvies liked me very much, so I made it my business to avoid him.

It was on one such day that I stole my first ride on the new railway. I had spent the morning greasing the leather flaps, and throwing stones at the rats, and by midday was looking for somewhere quiet to enjoy my lunch. I had noticed that the lead carriage was unattended and decided that it would be the perfect

Anthony O'Farrell

# THE ATMOSPHERIC RAILWAY

place to take a well deserved break. I quickly climbed aboard and settled into a seat, where I unwrapped and devoured my boiled egg, bread and pickle. Nobody knew where I was, and as the carriage was quite warm inside, I let my eyes rest for a few moments.

I awoke with a jolt. The train was moving. Anxious not to be discovered, I slid beneath the window like a guilty stow-away. I remained crouched until well clear of the foreman and his band of navvies. The train gently gathered speed and with the clickety-clack of wheel on track we meandered with a lazy motion in the direction of Dalkey.

We passed under a bridge, and silent images of the countryside rolled past my window. I waved to a small child and laughed at a silly dog chasing us. We soon out-ran the dog and continued to gather speed.

The carriage began to rattle and clatter, and then sway and lean into the curves. We rushed under another bridge with a whoosh of air. Faster, and the images began to flash past my window. Faster again, and I had to brace myself against the sway. The cold clammy realisation that something was wrong crept up my body.

I looked behind and saw that the carriage had not been coupled to the rest of the train. I struggled to my feet and clambered my way to the door. Outside, the air smashed into my face. I gripped the hand rail to recover my balance and set my feet firmly against the rocking carriage. Iron rails and wooden sleepers blurred in dizzy union below my feet as we hurtled forward, ever forward, ever faster.

I gripped the hand brake and pulled with all my might. Sparks flashed from beneath as the screech of metal against metal was drowned by the roaring wind. I pulled again, but the brake was no match for the piston's power. Signals, as useless and ineffective as my efforts, whizzed past. With every bend in the rail I expected to take flight, with every knock and bash to be torn apart. The

Anthony O'Farrell

# THE ATMOSPHERIC RAILWAY

noise was as thunderous as a battlefield, tugging, wrenching and straining. The end of the line came near, only one more corner. Vibrations shuddered through my bones. I winced against the dizzy nauseous speed, closed my eyes, and screamed.

It was then that I felt the hand of God and we began to slow. I saw the station house at Dalkey and felt the brake bite and grip. I pulled with one last effort and felt sure that every muscle and sinew in my arms would rip. We slowed to a stop and I cried like a baby.

*Frank Ebrington, 'The Fastest Man in the World.'*
*(84 mph Kingstown to Dalkey 1843.)*

Anthony O'Farrell

# THE COLLECTOR

He keeps her martini glass
from their last meeting,
holds it up to the light
of his apartment window.

It's always the same –
they have to go,
it's a matter of order –
tying things up
with a neat, tight bow,
a serial thing.

The translucent glass
holds a perfect imprint
of her plump, red lips.
At the base, a cherry
soaked in alcohol.
He twirls the crystal stem
between his fingers,
smiles,
unlocks the cabinet
and puts it on the top shelf
with all the others:
Marguerita, Amareto,
Tia Maria, Bloody Mary...

Alma Brayden

# MORNING RAGA, SANDYCOVE

How far the moon has pulled the tide
out past the sea-bruised stony side
of daily swimmers' harbour wall,
revealing limpets in their hide.

Great cumuli grow wide and tall,
spark distant rain in silver fall
their billow image stretches far
where boats slip out on second trawl.

The sea, a moving shimmer-star
that only angry winds could mar.
A seal lolls on a sloping rock,
gulls squabble, settle shellfish war.

Bright Oyster Catchers peck and knock
as cockles grip with stubborn lock.
Smart Turnstones shift through dry white bones
near pier where ferry waits in dock.

The people walk in broken rows
forget their losses and their woes
the sea recalls what each one knows:
that this day comes, that this day goes.

Alma Brayden

# MEMOIRS OF DISINTEREST

Fear drove them to the party, and when they arrived, Anger greeted them at the door. Inside they were introduced to Loathing, a lanky fellow wearing grey shaggy pants. He told them that Anxiety was out buying some more wine, and pointed out Self-Remorse in the corner who apparently had a good story to tell. The couple wasn't so sure as he looked a little sad. Self-Remorse had just finished smoking a joint with Disgust and Envy and was indeed feeling sorry for himself, again.

"Hi," said Miserable, "this is Guilty and his wife Panicky. And I'm Miserable. Great party eh?"

"It appears so," they replied. "I'm Sullen and this is Troubled. We've just flown in from the North."

Self-Remorse stood up at that point and brushed past them, saying "Don't eat the brownies man, they're not full of hash." And he walked off in search of Happiness.

Meanwhile, Cheerful had already found Happiness, a cute little blonde with the most amazing legs, and he was locked in the bathroom with her making one hell of a racket. Outside the door, Self-Conscious was waiting with Irritation

"What do you think they're doing in there?" said Irritation.

"Ask your Imagination," replied Self-Conscious.

"I can't, he stayed at home with Back Ache."

"Back Ache? I thought he was on holidays in France?"

Sir Real, always had interesting parties.

# MARCHÉ NOCTURNE

Serried poplars, pinkening sky
garlic and mussel scented air
guitar and accordion set up their cry-
it is time to dance at the night fair.

Plump and bald answer the call,
wives in hand, remembering when
these were sylph-girls at a Hunters' Ball:
thought they would always be young men.

Ancient lessons guide them round
on easy moving feet
that music such a familiar sound,
a happy lilting beat.

They look down with loving eyes,
smile through all the years
connectedness that never dies
enhanced by local wine, or beers

which ooze out of million pores
and stain two dozen shirts,
wives fatter now than years before
and wearing longer skirts

but in his eyes the very girl
he held so close back then,
this gentle move the self-same whirl:
Old bodies still contain young men.

Madeline A Stringer

# The Reluctant Visit

I glance up from my novel as my mother comes into the living room with my father's heavy Crombie overcoat. He follows her in and turns his back on her. She stands on tiptoe, so he can shrug his arms into the sleeves. He is going to the pub after all. Well he can go, but if she asks me to collect him, I won't. Not after the last time. I don't believe him when he says that, because he has had five heart attacks, he needs the whiskey to keep his old ticker going.

My mother takes a freshly-ironed handkerchief from the scratched sideboard and hands it to him. He pockets it, along with the extra pound note she slips him from the red purse that holds their money. My mother returns the purse to its position behind the statue of the Virgin Mary, which takes pride of place on the tiled fireplace of our house in Finglas.

After thirty years of being a housewife, she has returned to work in the local post office. My father only has a tiny pension from his job as a psychiatric nurse because he retired at fifty-five. All his life he hated "being locked up" as he called it, and she encouraged him to quit his job. He had wanted to be a garda, but he was told he was too light for his height. He is 6 foot one-and-a-half inches in his stockinged feet, as he tells anyone who asks. My father promises he will be back early from the pub.

"There is no rush, Ted", she says and throws more turf on the fire

She sits down in the worn armchair, and with bent fingers crochets a white matinee coat for a neighbour's child.

I live in a flat in Ballsbridge, and visit once a month, if I'm not too busy. She asks me will I have another slice of her homemade apple tart, but I tell her there are too many cloves in it for my liking. She says she will take out the cloves, but I say, don't bother. I scan my father's Irish Independent, and give her noncommittal answers when she asks me questions about work.

At ten o'clock she puts down the matinee coat, and shows me a

# THE RELUCTANT VISIT

bedspread she has made from spare pieces of wool. I hardly glance at it, and say the colours don't match. She doesn't say anything, but goes into the kitchen and makes a cup of tea. I continue reading the newspaper, and then I pick up my novel again. Every so often I see her glancing at the clock and I know what is coming next.

"I'm worried about your father."

"Don't be. He's always made his way home."

"Mr. O'Doherty had to bring him home last week."

"Mr. O'Doherty can bring him home this week."

"The O'Doherty's have gone to Ballybunion for a week's holiday."

"Ma, please don't ask me. He'll only shame me when I go into the pub."

"He's proud of you, that's all."

"He bores everybody, even the barman. 'This is my daughter who has a part in the films', he says. ' Do you want her autograph?' Nobody wants my autograph. I was only in one film. I die with shame when he goes on and on."

I pick up the newspaper again, and bring it up to my face. I have read all the advertisements twice over; all that is left are the sport pages. I hate sports. I put the paper down. My mother glances at the clock again and bites her lip. I can't bear her worried look and her bent grey head.

"OK," I say jumping up. "I'll get him, but this is the last time."

"Thanks Dolores, you're a star." she says, smiling.

I grab the keys to my cream Mini and rush out, slamming the door.

When I arrive at the pub, as gloomy as a cave, my father is sitting at the end of the long bar counter. Brownie, our collie dog, sits on the stool beside him, licking Guinness from an ashtray. A few middle aged women stand watching, and my father smiles, as proud as if Brownie was his firstborn. Blast, I think, now I will not

Maggie Gleeson

# THE RELUCTANT VISIT

only have a drunken father to get home, but a drunken dog as well.

"Johnny," my father calls to the barman, "another stout for Brownie, a glass for myself, and whatever the ladies are having."

The barman sees me. And raises his eyes to heaven. Then my father spots me.

"Dolores!" he shouts. "Come here. Ladies, have you met my famous daughter, Dolores. Dolores come here and give them your autograph. And Johnny, if you're quick with the drinks, she'll be after giving you her autograph as well. Won't you Dolores?"

"Da", I say, "nobody wants my autograph."

"Of course they do. She'll be in Hollywood soon. Elizabeth Taylor will be sending for her. Elizabeth was over to see Richard Burton work in the film "The Spy who came in from the Cold". And they gave Dolores a lift in their taxi from Ardmore. And she was in the Gresham Hotel with them, in their penthouse suite, if you wouldn't mind. Weren't you, Dolores? And tell them what happened, tell them, Dolores."

"Nothing happened."

"Well of course she has to say that. These stars stick together, don't they?" My father taps the side of his nose and winks.

I was only a bit player in "The Spy Who Came in from the Cold" and never even spoke to Richard Burton, so I had lied to my father when I said I had been in their penthouse suite, and that they had invited me to Hollywood. The barman had a bit part in the film also, so I know he is sniggering at me. Like he did the last time.

The barman smirks as he puts up the drinks. "That will be nineteen and sixpence, Ted," he says, his bony hand outstretched.

My father's long fingers move sixpences and pennies into piles.

"I only have fourteen shillings and sixpence. Strange that, I could have sworn I brought more with me."

The barman sniffs, his red-veined nose wrinkling.

"Here you are, Da," I say, giving him a ten shilling note.

Maggie Gleeson

# THE RELUCTANT VISIT

"Grand," he says, "will you have something yourself?"

"No, Da. Ma is waiting for you."

My father raises the glass of whiskey to his lips.

"I married a lovely women, Johnny, do you know that, a lovely woman."

"So you've told me Ted. I wish I was as lucky." My father drains the glass of whiskey, and gets down off the stool, swaying.

I take his arm and start to lead him out.

"Goodnight all," he says, "come along Brownie." Brownie stays on the stool, his head in the stout.

My father stops. "He wants time to drink his Guinness does our Brownie. Dogs have more sense that we do."

"Da," I say, " I can't wait any longer, call him again."

"Hold your horses, Brownie will come in his own good time. Look, he's finished." Brownie hops off the stool, wags his tail, and licks his lips over and over. The ladies laugh, and sip their gin.

Brownie runs between my father's legs, and my father sways.

"Are you all right there, Ted?" the barman asks.

"As right as rain. Have I told you, Johnny, my daughter works in the films?"

"I think you mentioned it, Ted." The barman sniffs again.

I manoeuvre my father through the door and over to my Mini which is on the far side of the road. When the air hits him, he sways even more, and I drape him over the passenger side, his arms across the roof of the car. I rush around to the driver's side to unlock the door. Then I see my father's arms sliding off the roof, and I run back, but he has already slipped to the ground. Brownie licks his face. My father says, "Good dog Brownie, good dog."

I lean down and try to lift him, but he is a dead weight. How dare he embarrass me like that? Why can't he hold his drink? Why is he such a stupid old fool? Now I will have to go in to that snotty barman and ask his help.

Maggie Gleeson

# THE RELUCTANT VISIT

"Fetch your mother," he says, "she will know what to do"

"I can't leave you here."

"Yes you can. Brownie will look after me. Go and get her."

I would love to drive off and leave them, but what if a passerby sees him abandoned on the ground? I stand there looking at him, and then I hear footsteps. I turn around and it is a tall young man in his late twenties with curly black hair. My type of man. When he sees my father, he rushes over.

"What happened, is he drunk?" he asks, watching Brownie lick my father's grinning face.

My father raises his head, "I'm not drunk, I can tip the end of my nose." He brings an unsteady finger towards his nose, but it veers past and hits his ear instead.

"Could you help get my father into my Mini? We live a quarter of a mile away."

"Of course." he says, and I like his direct gaze.

"Have you met my daughter, she is famous, in the films, would you like her autograph?" My father says looking up at us.

The man laughs. "Not at present, but I am delighted to meet her." He turns to look at me, his blue eyes sparkling. My face reddens.

Between the two of us we manage to haul my father to his feet, and we stagger to the Mini. Our hands touch as both of us settle my father's long legs into the front passenger seat.

"I can see a possible problem." says the young man.

"What's that?"

"How are you going to get your father out of the car when you arrive at your home?"

I know exactly what to do. The last time this happened, I ran in and got my mother and the two of us helped my father out of the Mini and in to the house. But I don't tell the young man that, because I don't want him to disappear on me.

# THE RELUCTANT VISIT

"Not sure," I say.

"Tell you what," the young man says "I'll sit in the back, and give you a hand when we arrive at your home."

He climbs into the back seat and laughs when my father says the reason that Brownie is hiccupping is that he had to drink his Guinness too quickly.

I like the sound of his laugh and wonder if he has a girlfriend.

"I'm Stephen," he says, as with strong shoulders and gentle hands, he helps my father out of the car.

"Stevie Wonder, my favourite," says my father, leaning against him.

"Glad you're home safe", my mother says opening the door.

Stephen guides my swaying father along the linoed hall and over to his armchair. My father collapses into the chair.

"Do you know what I'll have, Mammy?" he asks

"What Ted?"

"I'll have a cheese sandwich."

"I have it all ready for you, Ted." And there it is on the blue plate, the red cheddar peeping out between two slices of white bread. She has a sandwich like this prepared for him every night.

"Will you have a sandwich, Stephen?" she asks.

"I won't - I have to go into town." He gets up. "I can catch a bus on the corner."

"See Stephen to the door, Dolores" my mother says.

Outside the door Stephen says goodbye, and starts to walk down the path. Then he turns and comes back.

"You're very lucky to have parents who are proud of you, and who are settled into one another."

"I suppose I am."

"Would you be interested in coming to the pictures one evening?"

My heart skips a beat. Of course I am interested, very interested.

Maggie Gleeson

# THE RELUCTANT VISIT

"Yes," I say. He takes my phone number, then runs for the bus.

When I go back in, I ask my mother if I can have another slice of her apple tart.

As I look at my father asleep in the armchair, his head lolling to one side, his mouth open, I say to her, "How do you put up with Da's drinking?"

"I won't hear a word said against your father," my mother says, picking up her crochet, "He never said a cross word to me in his life." She looks at me and smiles.

"Nice boy Stephen. I thought the two of you looked well together." She stops crocheting. "Are you seeing him again?"

I nod, and smile back at her.

"We'll see you more often so."

# IN THE DISTANCE

there's a silver
pipe-like rocket
leaving chalk lines
over Howth Head,
then another
comes along
and slips across
its predecessor,
steely liners
air held buses
crossing oceans
linking nations,
packed with people
holding thoughts
and hidden notions,
tubes of thinking
conscious mortals
riding shotgun
through the blue
civilian sky

Billy Hutchinson

## An Gaeldia

Moṫaím mórṫímpeall orm í
cloisim ag súgraḋ i siansa duilliúraċ
na sailí is na fuinseoige í
feicim i nga gréine fánaċ
ar líon daṁáin alla í

meallaim as a sáiṁín ceo
aċ éalaíonn tart ar sléiḃte
ó Ṡliaḃ Liag go Calainn
ó 'eann Éadair go dtí
na Beanna Bóirċe

súnn neaċtar ó ṡúṫa craoḃ
s' ó fraoċóga ar na cloċḃallaí
aeraċa, luisne a gile go drithleaċ
ar muir, ar tír is ar éatar
á claoċlú féin de ṡíor


* buíoċas le Gabriel Rosenstock as ucht a ċabraċ leis an
dá ḋán i nGaeilge

Críona Ní Gháirbhí

# AN GAELDIA

I sense her all around me, playing
leafy symphony of alder, willow,
see her sunflash a stray cobweb.

Enticed from misty slumber,
she escapes through mountains, seas,
to Donegal and Clare, Howth and Mourne.

She sucks nectar from fraochogues, blackberries,
by soft green ditches, loose-knit walls.
Her brightness shines from mountain peaks.

She weaves my life from ancestral dreams.

Críona Ní Gháirbhí

# SNOW ANGEL

Legs silently shuffle
A track in freshly carpeted grass
As they scythe through the snow

Chasing flakes with outstretched tongue
Only catching water
The hunt to begin again

Snowballs part formed
Stuck to woollen gloves
In clumps of mischief

Arm raised over excited hatted head
Congealed clusters depart
Trickling through opened fingers

Landing between scarf and neck
On the warmth beneath
To shrills of frozen delight.

Joe McNally

## POISON

It was a long Saturday afternoon, and the tension in the house was beginning to choke me. Mum had been banging on at Dad for hours about not tiling the bathroom floor. So far he had remained stone-like on the sofa, pointing the remote control at the television. Flick, flick, flick. This was his usual tactic. I sat at the computer in the corner listening to music but I couldn't stop myself turning around automatically and watching each five-second screen shot on the TV. Flick. He stopped at the shopping channel. A woman was demonstrating some kind of electric vegetable juicer which came with a free set of glasses and 'if you order today, you will also get a vegetable peeler worth 9.99. Absolutely Free'. Dad sat, with this fake smile on his face, watching the carrots being annihilated like it was the best thing he had ever seen.

Mum came and stood in front of him blocking his view. Why does she have to do this? Why does she have to raise the ante every time? She knows what's going to happen. But there's no stopping her.

"So," she starts all high pitched and blamey-like. "You have you nothing to say. You have no excuses. You didn't forget. You didn't have something else to do. You just sat there all day watching television while I did my shift, went to the supermarket and cooked dinner?"

He moved his head to the left of her body and impatiently waved her away.

"Don't ignore me Jim. I'm telling you, I'm at the end of my tether. You're not working, you're bringing nothing into this house and you just sit there like a... a..." you could see her eyes wildly searching for the exact word that would push him over the edge, "cancer, sucking me dry." Yeah that'll do it. Down went the remote. Hands clenching the armchair, he pulled himself up and loomed over her. I touched my iPod, volume to 40. Eminem. I couldn't hear Dad's words but I could see her face going redder and redder.

# POISON

The tears would start any second. I needed to get out of the battle zone. An honourable retreat, I would say.

I passed Katie doing her homework at the kitchen table. Her head was down, chewing a clump of hair, pen steadily moving across the page. Oblivious to everything. She looked up at me with this abstract expression, like I was not there or else she was not there. I love that. I slammed the front door shut hoping that would make them stop arguing for a couple of minutes. I paused with the earphone off my ear. I heard her shouting, "Even your own son can't stand to be in the house." I zipped up my jacket and headed down towards Kilgobbet Park; some of the lads were bound to be there.

You could hear Maggot in the park before you could see him. He had been going on for weeks about getting a new airgun on eBay, and it had obviously arrived, as round after round ricocheted throughout the cold park. It was incredibly loud even with the sound of the motorway traffic in the distance. Maggot loves guns. As a result there are hardly any pigeons left in the Ballybrack area. I followed the sound and found him hidden in some bushes at the far side of the playing fields. He was lying flat with the gun perched on his shoulder and some class of a scarf tied around his head.

"Maggot."

"Jesus, Titch, keep your head down."

"Who is the target?"

"There is an armed patrol on manoeuvres due in 5,4,3,2,1."

A group of girls that we knew were walking by. Lisa O'Dwyer was one of them. I've only fancied her since sixth class. I ducked down. Oh God, she'll think I am so lame, playing with guns with Maggot of all people, like a big kid. Maggot let off a couple of rounds in their direction. The girls turned around and started screaming and laughing all at the same time. I looked up and Lisa O'Dwyer was laughing too but when she saw me, she kind of stopped and then

# POISON

she smiled straight at me. Like she was saying, I know it's lame and gay but it's ok.

Maggot jumped up and waved the gun in the air.

"Praise be to Allah. Death to the infidels. Praise be to Jihad." This was too much for the girls and they shook their heads and marched on.

"You're spending way too much time on Assassins Creed, you eejit." I said laughing.

He looked funny with his white hair and skinny arms waving in the air. Maggot doesn't have proper friends, but he counts me as one even though I am constantly slagging him off to the rest of the lads. You can't help it with Maggot, he just seems to be asking for it.

We decided to go down to the off license. Maggot had a tenner to buy some cans and I'd got my brother Mikey's ID which he gave me before he went to Australia for a year, last summer. He is living on a beach somewhere surfing and being a general pisshead. Lucky him. I like having the bedroom to myself but I miss talking to him. He told me once, when they were having a real barney downstairs, that he remembers when Mum and Dad actually liked each other and sat on the couch together and went to the pub together and even slept in the same bed together. That was years ago when I was little, and before Dad's business went bust.

I bought the cans without too much trouble and went back into the park. Two older lads from our estate, Bosco and Rob, were there drinking their own cans. I was glad to see them partly because hanging out with Maggot can be like hanging out with an annoying little brother and partly because Bosco's girlfriend, Ciara, happens to be best friends with Lisa O'Dwyer and maybe there would be some chance of hooking up with them later. We knocked back two cans each as quickly as we could and the evening began to feel all glow-y like. Then out of nowhere Bosco suggested that we call up to Lisa's house. Lisa's Mum, he said, is working and her Dad lives in

# POISON

Dubai so it is more or less a constant free house.

Me, Maggot, Bosco and Rob turned up at Lisa's door like four losers but she seemed happy enough to see us and let us in. Her house is really modern with cream leather sofas everywhere and a 40" TV hanging on the wall. In the kitchen, the music was blaring, and I could see a gang of girls were drinking Smirnoff Ice and straightening each other's hair. Myself and Maggot had a couple more cans each and we watched a bit of Premier League action on Sky Sports but it was really boring. I went to see if I could find Lisa, but she was laughing with her friends and she barely looked up as I came in. She kept on talking like I was invisible or something. I went upstairs to the bathroom. On the landing was a huge collage of photographs of Lisa, her Mum and her Dad. Photographs on the beach, in the snow, at school plays, on airplanes, cute photographs of Lisa opening a huge Santa present, less cute photographs of Lisa with train tracks in her mouth and in all of them everyone was smiling. They look all really healthy and happy, like a family from some American sit-com.

I went into this huge bathroom with black shiny tiles on the floors and the walls. Without thinking, I opened the medicine cupboard and rooted through the plasters and the scissors and the asprin and the half used packs of antibiotics. I didn't know what I was looking for but then I spotted a bottle of Xanax at the back of the top shelf. I stood there looking at them. The prescription on the bottle was made out to Lisa's mum, so maybe not exactly happy families after all. Automatically I just popped four into my mouth and washed it down with water flavoured with mint from the toothpaste holder. I took a slug of lager and sat on the side of the bath and looked at my reflection in the black tiles. I was beginning to feel paranoid - the way Lisa ignored me downstairs was eating into me. All the good feelings I had felt in the park were gone. I thought of calling Mikey but I didn't have enough credit

# POISON

and besides I couldn't work out what time it was in Australia. Early morning I think. Mikey is not an early morning person. After a few minutes a warm energy spread out from my stomach to my limbs and finally up to my brain. As I floated downstairs, I got a text. It was from Katie. "Where r u." I felt a knot in my stomach thinking of her lying in her bed worrying about a fool like me instead of dreaming about pony clubs or whatever little girls dream about. I texted her back, "I'm ok, go to sleep."

Back downstairs, the music had got even louder and more people had arrived. Maggot was talking to no-one in particular about whether Call of Duty was better than Halo. Rob had disappeared. Bosco and Ciara were staring at Maggot but you could tell they weren't listening. My arms and legs were beginning to feel like they had weights sewn into my muscles, so I went into the kitchen to get some water. Rob was leaning against a girl whose back was against the fridge. I recognised Lisa's pink sparkly nails digging into Rob's shaved head. I ducked out of the room. Oh God. Rob. I should have known. I mean Bosco and Rob always travel in pairs.

I could hear Maggot still droning on. He was really getting on my nerves.

"Jesus, Maggot, would you ever shut up. Nobody cares, you albino freak."

Maggot just smiled and went on talking. There was this black cloud in my head.

I don't know how long I sat there, maybe it was hours, maybe it was just a few minutes. I kept thinking of Lisa's face smiling at me and then thinking of Rob's big ugly hands all over her. I couldn't stand it. I stood up and somehow weaved my way into the kitchen. Rob and Lisa were still hard at it but now she was sitting on the worktop with her legs wrapped around him. I ran at Rob and threw myself on his back. "What the fuck!" he shouted. I started hitting at his neck. He dug his elbow into my chest and somehow turned

# POISON

around. I kept hitting him. I knew now that I had crossed the line and that I was either going to take a beating or walk away the victor. It felt kind of good, because there was no choice now. I hit his head and face really fast. His nose started bleeding. I could hear Lisa screaming. But I was beyond caring. I kept hitting him until my arms started to slow down despite myself. Then with one movement, he pushed me to the ground and sat on my chest. His knees pinned down my arms. I looked up at him. The blood from his nose was mixed with spit from his mouth and I realised he was really angry. I saw the arm go back, the fist clenched. My face exploded with pain.

The next thing I knew I was being pulled out of the kitchen and out of the house. I tried hitting whoever was pulling me. But my arms wouldn't work anymore. I remembered thinking that I was going to get the shit kicked out of me and somehow that was fine by me. But nothing happened. No blows came. I looked up. There was Maggot looking at me and he was holding his head and there was blood streaming down his face. Then he started howling into the night like some demented dog and I had to laugh out loud at the state of him.

# CIRCLE TIME

intertwined
bodies swirling
in circle union

floating
in silence
all is said

they dance
forever
in perfect circle
time

Philipp Herrmann

## SNOW LEOPARD

They say you cannot roar,
that you live silent as a saffron
monk aware of avalanches.

Every part designed
for high, lonely living,
you prefer cloud-muffled

silence where you can hear
an icicle drop, the leap of a ghost
hare or hoof-slip of a reckless markhor.

Your fur, piled thick as a drift
patterned with smoky rosettes,
tail, long as the snowy plume

trailing a high plane
keeps you balanced,
a warm blanket when asleep.

Tufted white feet
wide as snowshoes,
help you slip away

far from the sight
of lens or rifle
into a secret world.

Blasted from the Hindukush
to Siberia, mysterious animal
live on in your fierce beauty.

Alma Brayden

# DEATH IN THE DUBLIN MOUNTAINS - CH 2

*(In Chapter 1 some old bones are found buried on a golf course)*

Kevin signed in at Glenwood police station. There was a note on his desk asking him to meet the Super.

"What now?"

The Dept. probably had another communication from the new minister. Another scheme to be implemented. They were getting very good at handling these schemes. Anything "the boys" didn't like got sabotaged. Kevin now had so much experience in this station that he relished the various methods they thought up to avoid implementing them. He also realised that whatever officer whose section was involved would be up the wall about it.

At the same time the boss, being the political animal he was, always complied with the directives, and usually it was Kevin who got the job of co-ordinating them. He was regarded as a safe pair of hands.

Kevin was right.

He was being assigned to organise and liaise with a new group due to convene in the station. That meant finding a vacant room and setting up some equipment. He also knew that this would involve the Juvenile Liaison Officer.

He looked at the information on the group due to start the course.

"An Introduction to the latest American Methods of Organising Juvenile Liaison Officers and their Intra- and Inter-Psychological Implications. Special Attention to be paid to Cultural Complications arising from Recent Immigration Policy."

This, thought Kevin, was going to be a real beauty.

For a start he knew that nobody would understand the word "Intra". Indeed he wasn't too sure he understood it himself.

"Recent Immigration Policy" meant: "Send them all back where they came from."

Mary Hanlon

# DEATH IN THE DUBLIN MOUNTAINS - CH 2

Worst of all, experience told him that the crowd attending this would be all the headcases every Government department wanted out of the office for whatever reason, probably so that they could get some work done without wild objections.

He saw the recently assigned J.L. officer come down the corridor. She was a gorgeous looking woman. She was also very good at her job and well liked.

"Kevin, we have hit the Jackpot this time. Did you see what's coming in? This lot will be more trouble than any crim. locked in the cells. What am I going to do? Is there any way you could get me out of this? I haven't the faintest notion what they will be talking about. I was not all that hot on the jargon when I was in college".

"Look, the Super forgot that he agreed to this. I expect he owes some other crowd a favour, and they dumped this on him. Anyway we have some time to set this up. Find out from the tulip giving the course what kind of equipment he will need."

She looked glum at the thought of the coming conference.

"Ah, come on Angela. We'll all give you a hand. Look, set up tea in the canteen first and show them around the place. Make sure they see a few really tough cases and that will knock the stuffing out of them before they start. Come on, it won't be that bad. And it will look good on your C. V."

She cheered up.

"You will help me won't you?"

"Of course I will, I'll get all the lads to pitch in too".

"God Kevin I love you. You're terrific."

Before he knew it she threw her arms around him and kissed him.

With the physical contact his whole body come alive.

"Good Christ," he swore to himself, "Why do they do this to me?

So many women I meet think I'm made of stone. They all think

# DEATH IN THE DUBLIN MOUNTAINS - CH 2

I'm past it. A bloody teddy bear going round at the bottom."

He moved away so quickly, she knew she had overstepped the mark.

"I'm sorry; I shouldn't have done that."

"Forget it. It's the slagging I'll get if we are seen."

Please God let her accept this reason.

She did.

"I didn't think", she said.

Women never do, he thought sourly.

"Oh, come on snap out of it. You can't go around blaming every woman you meet for your middle age reactions."

It didn't take him long to set up the room for the meeting. As he finished a trip to the canteen to coax the staff there to give a bit of extra care to the incoming group, he was called to the Super's office again.

The boss was standing at the office window looking longingly at the distant mountains.

"There's no city on earth like Dublin. How many places can you just look at a view like that? If I look in the other direction I can see the sea. If I open the window the air will be pure and fresh." He sighed dramatically.

Kevin had heard all this before. He resisted the impulse to point out that not all workers had a beautiful office and a beautiful view, and that most modern offices were climate controlled and no window could be opened. Indeed he could make a joke about the customers in this particular establishment wanting to put windows to uses other than breathing fresh air. In fact most of them had a great aversion to it.

He knew better than to say anything like this.

The next bit of the monologue would be about God and his goodness. In fact he could even be treated to a few lines of the poet Padraig Pearse about "mountainy men near to the gates of heaven."

# DEATH IN THE DUBLIN MOUNTAINS - CH 2

There were times when he thought the boss had completely lost it. He knew a lot of employees had the same feelings about their particular boss. It amazed him at times how large institutions functioned at all.

However there was a surprise in store for him.

"Kevin you are in luck. We just had a call from a golf club in the Dublin Mountains about some bones that turned up on the course. I was just about to go when I heard that the minister is coming to open the conference so I have to stay here and meet him myself. I thought I would get a few holes played up there. I believe it's a fantastic development. Big money. Important people. I have just had the owner on the phone. O'Hara's his name. Of course, as he pointed out, the bones are the carcass of some old cow that a local farmer was too mean, or afraid it had a notifiable disease like foot and mouth, to send it to a knackers yard. So he simply buried it on the golf course. He invited me out to play anytime. O'Hara's a real gentleman of the old school. He says he wants to apologise in advance for wasting police time but some fussy old civil servant who found the bones is making a big drama out if it. He insisted on calling us. I know you will take care of this case very quickly. There is big money involved. The wrong sort of publicity could do harm. The major tourist organisations might get to hear of it There would be questions asked about hygiene and health and safety. O'Hara asked us to be as discreet as possible when dealing with this case. He emphasised that he did not want any favours or to interfere with the investigation in any way. A real well educated gentleman. Not like the jumped up johnnies we usually meet up with."

As he was about to leave, the boss called him back.

"And Kevin will you take the new trainee with you. Head office can't say we did not give her "appropriate training" this time. A trip to the mountains on a fine sunny day. She can't come to any harm

# Death in the Dublin Mountains - Ch 2

and we can dress the outing up in all sorts of jargon to suit whatever they have in the training manual."

He was very pleased with himself for thinking of this idea.

"She is very pretty. You know what I think about that. You are a safe pair of hands."

Kevin well knew what the boss thought. He had heard it often enough.

"Human nature is human nature." That was quoted many times. No matter how many directives he got from Headquarters there was no way if it could be avoided that he would let one of the "red blooded young men," as he called the regular officers, out with any young female.

Women's Liberation might as well never have happened as far as the Super was concerned. As he didn't want him to have a heart attack, Kevin never suggested that the females be rostered with a homosexual. They did not exist in the force as far as he was concerned. Indeed he never faced up to the fact that they existed at all. He simply did not believe in it.

He went to the Day Room to collect the new trainee.

"Pretty" did not do this young woman justice. She was breathtakingly beautiful. No young man, "red blooded" or otherwise, could resist that beauty.

What about an old man?

What about me?

You are a safe pair of hands, he told himself wryly.

Kevin explained the job they had been given.

She was very enthusiastic.

"I thought I was going to be kept filing car registrations forever," she said.

# I SEE YOU

The metal waste paper bin stood in the corner of the ward. It was grey, battleship grey. Someone had put a light white plastic bag inside for ease of emptying. It was the rustle of this bag that first caught my attention. A faint rustle at first, then becoming more insistent. I hoped it wasn't a mouse or God forbid a rat. It was impossible to take my eyes off the bin so keen was I to see what it would reveal. I wasn't disappointed.

The head appeared first, smooth, rounded and white. The eyes beady black, unswerving in their gaze. What terrified me slightly was the beak, long, yellow and curved. It seemed to take an age and some effort for the bird to fully reveal itself. I realized then that it was a seagull. The grey of it's wings was several shades paler than the bin on which it was perched. I wondered why the bin didn't topple over with its weight.

Just as the plastic began its frantic rustle again the seagull spread its wings and almost silently took flight. Immediately it was joined by its mate.

I felt calm and peaceful as I watched the slow elegant circling of the two birds' flight. Confined within the space of the ward I marvelled at their graceful movement, the steady sound of their wings beating the stale air of the room.

It wasn't until a little while later that I wondered about the occupants of the other beds. Scanning the room I realised no one was paying the gulls any attention. Some had visitors anyway and the old woman beside me was always sleeping.

It was the sudden clang of the bin overturning that brought my attention back to it. Now more seagulls were coming out in quick succession. At this stage there was a frantic quality to their flying. Soon the ceiling was obscured by their flailing bodies, wings beating against each other and the confines of the room. I was more and more aware of the cacophony, the thumping of bodies throwing

Sandra McTurk

# I See You

themselves against hard surfaces, the tapping of beaks against glass and the overriding noise of their cawing and squawking.

Frustrated now by my own immobility, I grabbed the bell and pressed it urgently again and again. At last the nurse came. "Open the window, please open the window" I begged, "let them out". It seemed to take ages to make her understand. She stood looking long and hard at me.

"Och a few birds won't do a wee girl like you any harm" she said.

Raising myself up as far as I could in the bed, with finger flapping and pointing I said "Look open the window, they're hurting themselves, there's blood"

This time the nurse responded. The window was opened. The birds in orderly fashion exited the room. Sinking back into the pillows I watched them go, flying to freedom in a blue sky.

They stopped the morphine after that.

Sandra McTurk

# CARTOGRAPHERS

Uncertain only as to which monarch
would underwrite their madness
their loyalty was maritime:
the gnawing breeze, the prow's
surge and fall that scattered
hoar on the trackless ocean.
Their intimacy was with trade and line,
with the minute limit of the azimuth,
and the slow tilt of constellations.
What hunger impelled them
to cast fortune to the winds
and cross the uncharted horizon?

Upon those shores that vindicated their folly
they left the indifferent flags, like spores.

Dave Butler

# HAPPINESS

When I first met you
The moon sipped the stars
Kissed the blueberry bush
Danced with the snowman
Birds romanced in the trees
Whistled in the dawn
The sun scooped up the clouds
And opened up the morning.

Maggie Gleeson

## THE PROPOSAL

They had had their usual weekend. Saturday morning meant a wamase round the supermarket to get their provisions for that nights dinner and the requisite 'after dinner treat'. This was followed up with that always exciting trip to the newsagents, he for the paper and her for whatever magazine caught her fancy. Time permitting, they would go for a coffee and a muffin, smoothie for herself, her not being a coffee drinker, and if not, then it was straight home for whatever the rest of the day brought.

Truth be told, the whole thing had been a bit of a shock and the last thing that he had expected her to talk about the following morning. You know those lazy Sundays when you wake up against your better judgement, disgruntled by the redness of your eyelids as they reflect the sunshine peeking in through the gap in the curtains, hoping to have seen blackness instead? And even though you have nothing that needs doing you know that you are going to have to open your eyes some time during the day so why not right then. This wasn't one of those mornings.

The darkness still cast its invisible shadow across the room when he felt her snuggle in beside him. Turning his neck he caught the luminous movement of the minute hand on his alarm clock as it moved vertical to indicate the passing of another hour. '6am is for weekdays' he mumbled to no-one in particular turning back to try and find his comfy spot, certain in the knowledge that it was gone for ever. When his eyes had adjusted to the room, he saw her face turned up to his. Braving the elements of his bad breath and drool, she put her head on his shoulder and rested her permanently cold feet on his always warm legs. As per usual, he thought a cuddle was just her want.

All blue eyes, bed head, and bravery, out it came in a whisper, "Will you marry me?"

In fairness she'd been talking about it for a while but he had just smiled at every mention thinking her more ponderous than

Joe McNally

## The Proposal

anything else, and definitely not serious. Nonetheless, his response was instantaneous. "Yes. Of course I will."

He knew that everyday conversation from then on was going to be different - full of questions whose answers would go unheeded regardless of what he said. He couldn't help but wonder what input he was going to have at all. Typical Princess. For now, all he could do was smile his smile of love at her as he had a thousand times before.

Wrapping his arm around her he leaned over to whisper and in response she tilted her head.

"Its very early my love, now go back to your room for a snooze before you wake your mother".

"Ok Daddy." she sighed and climbing over him she silently found the floor and tip-toed her way back to her bed.

"What's all the commotion?" his wife asked.

"Oh nothing dear," he replied, "just my other woman".

# AG ÉISTEACHT SIAR

(i.m. m ó Díreáin, file)


cloiseann sé damhsóirí beoga
go díograiseach i Seit an Chláir
mná chomh héadrom le cleití
fir ag bacráil ar úrlár dúlice
ceol béil is fidle ón am atá imithe


cuimhníonn sé ar am an anró
ach spréachann tine mhóna go glé
sa chistin bheag chlutar cois claí
na píobairí gríosaí ina dtost go deo


Críona Ní Gháirbhí

# LISTENING BACK

(i.m. máirtín ó díreáin)

he hears set-dancers
women light on feet
men battering
to fiddle-music
on black-flagged floor

singers remember
troubled times
turf-fire crackles
under the thatch

now the piper of the ashes
pipes no more

Críona Ní Gháirbhí

# WRITING BLUES

The teak door
dark and impenetrable
frustrates me
I beat at it shamelessly
willing it to dissolve.
Impatient, I busy myself
with important things
that just have to be done
like washing and shopping
thinking about birthdays
school reports
and what's for dinner.

But sometimes late at night
the door cracks open and I sneak in
to stare in wonder at the jars on the shelf
filled with remembrances
ideas I barely recognize
making my heart lurch
As I stretch up
to take the jars down
they slip through greasy fingers
fall crashing to the ground
the contents disappear
like summer rain on sand.

Eileen Counihan

# IN THE WILD

I felt the fresh warm air filling my nostrils as I breathed in deeply; it smelt of soil – the Zimbabwean countryside. Larry's huge frame filled the passenger seat beside me. Taking a slug of beer, he said to me,

"This is the life, Mike. I feel like a lion relaxing in the midday heat."

I glanced quickly at him, as he smiled at me. I detested his tobacco stained teeth.

"If only I'd a lioness in the back seat!"

It was the first time that we had been so far out of Harare where we were working in an engineering company. We were from the UK and on a two year contract. Larry's eyes roamed from one side of the road to the other as he took in the different farms we were passing. We saw huge irrigated fields of wheat. These carpets of green were amazing; they were part of agribusinesses that had their own reservoirs with thousands of litres stored from the rainy season. Then we went by poor farming land where goats and cattle grazed on sparse brown grass. Here there were no crops under irrigation. We saw some women carrying buckets on their heads which I presumed was their daily supply of water, and others with heavy bundles of firewood. Some of the children with them walked barefoot.

Although this main route heading for Zambia was relatively quiet, friends had told me that as we got nearer to the game reserve to look out for animals. We might see zebra or buffalo or even a lion or elephant crossing the road. I was about to see things I had never encountered before. As I drove, my mind moved from image to image as I recalled various books I'd been reading, with their magnificent photographs of the Victoria Falls as well as of life in the wild. I thought of pictures of herds of buffaloes and a pride of lions in the game reserve to which we were driving.

Neither of us had any experience of being amongst animals, and the idea of sleeping in an unfenced campsite set my heart pounding

Andrew Furlong

# IN THE WILD

with excitement, but also with apprehension. I rehearsed the advice
I'd received from colleagues at work who knew the wild. They'd told
me to watch out for baboons when cooking, otherwise they'd hop
up and steal the steaks off the barbeque. They'd said to keep my
distance from the river or a watering pool if out of the car, because
crocodiles can move much quicker than I'd think. I wished that at
least one of these people was with us now. I was worried that Larry's
desire to get good photographs would lead to him trying to get too
close to the animals. I'd asked him more than once to promise not
to take risks. Larry had reassured me that he wasn't a fool, he knew
animals could be highly dangerous and he'd several lenses for long
distance shots, but despite that I didn't trust him.

In the weeks leading up to this trip, he had kept up a front of
bravado. He loved to have a beer in his hand and to emulate the
tough Afrikaners he met in Harare. He'd never told me till today
that he been having nightmares of being dragged in his sleeping bag
out of our tent by a lion.

We arrived about four o'clock at the game reserve on the banks of
the Zambezi, after a long hot journey and parked our car. I watched
the cloud of dust churned up by our vehicle as it was blown away
by the wind.

"No room in the camp site tonight, guys, but you can book for
tomorrow and the next day, but then we're full up for the weekend
I'm afraid," said the Park Ranger in the office.

"That's disappointing," I said, "but I guess we should have
contacted you earlier."

"We'll book now," said Larry, "how much for two nights?"

"Forty dollars."

I produced some notes from the back of my khaki shorts. The
Ranger said we could arrive at the camping area any time after noon.

"Do you think we'll see the big five?" Larry asked.

"At this time of year leopard or cheetah unlikely, but you should

# In the Wild

see the others and certainly the elephants," said the Ranger. "I suggest you go to the motel this evening near Customs, it has a camping site."

"Great," Larry said, "we will."

On arriving at the motel, we first ordered some beers. Larry persuaded me that it wasn't worth going to the trouble of putting up our tent, seeing it was only for one night, and that anyway it would be fun to sleep under an African sky. Though I was reluctant at first, I agreed – that was after my second beer. We found an empty space close to a large marula tree, some forty feet high. We sat outside the bar as darkness fell quickly after sunset. After several more cold beers, we went across to the barbeque and helped ourselves to steaks, chops, chicken, sausages and salads. We still found everything incredibly cheap.

After our meal, we drank more beers and chatted and relaxed in the warm evening air with a full moon beaming down on us. When I say chatted, what I really mean is that I listened as Larry regaled me with one story after another, many of them of a coarse nature and involving his various exploits with women. What they found attractive about him I could never work out, he was often unshaven and untidily dressed. We were in bed about eleven. For a while I gazed up at the African star-filled sky, wondering would Larry's snoring keep me awake.

"What a sight, so many stars," I thought, as I closed my eyes and turned over on my side.

I was still trying to get to sleep when a noise startled me. It was an elephant stripping the marula tree of its fruit, which hung like large sausages from the branches. It was tearing leaves and small branches off the tree as well as the juicy fruit. Looking up at it from ground level it appeared massive; I was both shocked and scared, and very worried that Larry would wake up and let out a loud curse. That could frighten the elephant and maybe make it attack us. I

# IN THE WILD

reached over and shook him gently till he woke up, whispering to him about our visitor. I knew that one swish of the elephant's trunk or its foot on our rib cages would be fatal. We watched in silence. I was amazed at how high the elephant could reach with its trunk. Fortunately, after a few minutes it ambled off.

"Wow," said Larry in a tense voice "that could have been nasty." He sounded more subdued than usual.

"He knew we were lying at his feet," I said.

"Yea, maybe, but supposing he'd reckoned we were in his way. He might have swished us to one side with his trunk. And broken God knows how many bones in our bodies; that's if he didn't kill us outright."

"The locals would have known not to sleep under a marula tree," I said. "We should have checked out with the waiters whether we'd picked a good place to sleep."

Larry grunted and turned over on his side, yawning loudly.

"I don't know if I'll get back to sleep again. Should we sleep in the car or find some chairs inside the motel?" I asked him.

"It won't be much different tomorrow night, there's no fence around the camp site," he replied.

I thought of Sally, my girlfriend back in the UK, who'd be worried sick if she knew what risks we were taking.

"Hundreds of foreign tourists and the game loving folk here come each year. You don't read of too many accidents. I guess we'll survive," Larry said.

"How many impala or baby zebras have been hunted down and devoured in the last few hours within a mile or two? We're in a killing zone," I said. I was still feeling very anxious that another elephant might arrive at any minute.

"Listen let's get some sleep, hopefully we'll see plenty of animals during the day," Larry said.

The next morning we were on our way by eight o'clock. The sun

# IN THE WILD

was shining and the skies were blue.

"I took a small map yesterday from the office, there are a number of roads through the reserve," I said. "We'll have at least three hours to drive around before we can enter the campsite at noon."

"I can't wait to start shooting. I hope I get some really great photos."

"On the map it says that you should remain in your car when you're in the reserve, so don't get out and annoy a bloated lion basking in the sun by asking it to smile nicely."

"No need to, you know I've several lenses."

The different routes through the reserve were well signposted. Impalas were the first animals we saw. They were grazing about fifty yards from the road as we approached, but then the ones on guard heard the engine and caught its smell in the wind. In seconds, they were bouncing across the open vlei like ballerinas with their tails bobbing and the white undersides showing the ones behind the direction in which they were racing away.

"Impressive," I said.

"I wasn't expecting them to flee so quickly. Next time we see some in the distance let's stop and then I can start photographing as we move slowly forwards. The light is so bright; it's great for my shots."

"Look to the right. Do you see the three giraffe?"

Larry clicked furiously. A jeep came from the other direction, raising a stream of dust behind it, and the giraffes turned from browsing on the leaves and raced away.

"You wouldn't call them ballerinas," I said, sniffing the air and catching the smell of dung from the roadside. "How ungainly they look when they run."

We left the vlei which bordered each side of our route, enabling us to see four or five hundred yards in each direction, and entered an area of much denser growth with small trees and bushes as well

# IN THE WILD

as plenty of tall ones right up to each side of the road.

"We won't be able to see anything now," I said.

"I wonder how long this will last," Larry said, putting his camera on his lap.

"Don't forget you may see some birds up in those trees, they're very colourful."

I steered the car round a sharp bend and then braked hard. Yards away there was a stream of elephants coming out of the dense undergrowth to cross the road and disappear into the bush on the other side. As well as fully grown elephants there were baby elephants sticking close to their mothers. One of the mothers turned towards us, after pushing back a baby elephant emerging from the trees. She was clearly concerned. She opened her ears spreading them wide and made a trumpeting sound that made me instantly put the car into reverse.

"Don't move," said Larry quickly. "Remember you were advised to stay still, unless they come charging at us."

He had his camera to his eye; I supposed he couldn't believe his luck. After a minute or two the large elephant poked her trunk into the undergrowth and, taking hold of the baby's trunk, pulled it forward, and then crossing over disappeared. We had to stay for ten minutes till all the elephants had passed by. Some took no notice of us while a few stopped and stared, and one trumpeted a warning sound.

"Unforgettable," I said, "what fine animals they are. And wasn't the bull impressive?"

"Did you notice the damage to his tusks? Maybe that happened when he fought to become head of the herd."

"I've read there's often fierce competition," I added. "At least there weren't a few of them fighting under that marula tree last night."

We drove on and entered another expanse of vlei. I stopped the

Andrew Furlong

# IN THE WILD

car; in the far distance, looking through binoculars, I saw that there were buffalo and kudu, as well as some impala. Nearer to us were about twenty baboons which raced about and screamed; a mother came bounding over to the road and scooped a small one up and ran off with it to safety.

"This is such an amazing place," said Larry, "I could stay here for weeks. I'd love to be in a viewing hut at night to photograph the action."

"Twenty-four seven here, there's always something going on, it's a question of being fortunate enough to be in the right place at the right time," I said.

"True enough and also not being in the wrong place at the wrong time," said Larry with a sneer. "You have hippos to look forward to tonight, they'll come up from the river and pass through our site to go and graze, hyenas will be scavenging, lions might decide on something other than impala meat and snakes will be moving around too."

"You can have the tent, it's all yours. I'm bagging the back seat for the next two nights. If I'm going to be the driver I need some sleep, especially with such a long journey home," I said, deciding that I wasn't going to take unnecessary risks.

"Coward," said Larry. "What'll your girlfriend think when she hears about it?"

# Entertrainment

Join a link
from location
clunk of the iron
under wheel
lean on a pole
amble the aisle
trip to the town
end of the line
follow a track
shift to the left
rolling steel path
leans to the right
year upon year
onward and on
no-one gets lost
bearings are found
returning home
minding the gap
pssshh.

Billy Hutchinson

## AFTER THE RAIN

He had large
hob nail boots
thick hands
a grin that wouldn't quit

the child
on two new wheels
coloured balloons
tied to his bike

nerves
of the boy
bigger
than the man's shadow

overlapping
with laughter
and the joy
of a proud grandfather

'don't let go granda!
don't let go!'
'I won't
I promise, I won't'

but the lie
was sweeter
than the smell
of the wet grass.

Billy Hutchinson

# BROKEN

Emily is keeping a sharp eye on the advancing swarm of crows. Some of them are awfully close but they have not seen her yet.

Which is good cos Emily needs to Focus. Miss Mooney, her First Class Teacher, would be proud of how hard she is Focusing right now. She has to Find her Daddy. This table is his favourite hiding place when they play hide and go seek so it stands to reason that he's here. They all came home from the hospital a whole two days ago now. He's not in any of the rooms and he can't fit underneath the stairs like she can. He must be under here.

She can see Mummy. The crows are all either hovering around her or pecking at the food. They are making so much Noise. It's so they can cover up the pain in the air. That way Mummy mightn't feel bad anymore. Emily feels sorry for them. Being noisy doesn't work. She knows. She tried it once for one whole day. The Shhhh Day.

On that day, when Emily got up the radio wasn't on so Mummy could hear the news and the cat wasn't purring on the couch. He was still sitting on the window outside waiting to be let in. Breakfast time wasn't even chatty. Even BABY Michael didn't talk forever as usual.

Emily being a big girl - seven and a half, nearly growed up, asked will she set the table cos Granma showed her how. Mummy says nothing. Emily lets Mummy know that she can reach the bowls herself. Mummy stays quiet. Mummy doesn't say, Mummy doesn't move, so Emily and Michael sit at the table cos they don't know what else to do.

Sometimes when they are bold Mummy says "Be Quiet!" and they are and then it is alright again, so they stay still and quiet until the big hand is at twelve and the little hand is at nine. It is Time For School. Mummy doesn't say so but Emily knows this cos Daddy teaches her Big Girl stuff like this so she can learn to be a Good Big Sister.

Kate McGrath

# BROKEN

They have to go to school so Emily pushes back her chair. She tells it not to be noisy but it doesn't listen. Mummy jumps at the noise of the chair. Emily's heart jumps too cos Mummy has moved for the first time this morning. Mummy says "Goodbye loves" to the window she's been looking at all morning.

The hungry cat is not pleased that he is being ignored like this. He is row-ling at the window. But Emily cannot let him in. He is noisy. And Today is Shhhh Day.

Emily and Michael walk carefully and quietly, Emily takes Michael's hand to make sure he does too, across the kitchen floor and go to school. They don't know the way but Charlie Johnson's Mum is outside squished into her car and Charlie is too and they know the way so Emily takes Michael's hand and they get into the car. As they drive away Charlie's Mum says: "Oh you poor darlings. How is your poor Mummy holding up?" And Emily says fine.

Charlie is fun but Not fun on the "Shhhh Day" cos in Emily's tummy is a funny feeling cos - she's not sure why.

By the time school is over Emily has made a Decision. Emily is going to make noise. Then Mummy will say "Stop it, Emily!" and the Shhhh Day will be over cos Mummy will not be Quiet any more. Then Emily will know that everything will be alright. It will so work! Wait 'til you see!

So Emily made noise, BIG NOISE. She ran across the hallway in BIG LOUD STEPS and SHOUTED "HELLO MUMMY!" but Mummy said nothing and she would have stopped long before Granma's eyes burned her into the ground and her voice rumbled "Try to be a good girl Emily."

She just kept thinking if she could BE LOUD for a little longer the Shhhh Day would go away and her Mummy - her proper Mummy - could come back.

The next morning the crows have gone. In the house is Mummy

Kate McGrath

# BROKEN

and Michael and Emily. Emily is back under the table. It is a Big Table and there are plenty of corners she could have missed where Daddy could be.

When her knees get red angry at the carpet she stops, thuds down on her bottom and thinks. Her heart goes thud, thud, thud.

The door opens and Emily's heart jumps so high she bangs her head. But she doesn't cry. She sees feet and knows her banged head is stupid Michael's fault. His stupid black shoes aren't even tied. Daddy showed her and Michael how and all but babies forget everything. She sighs. Crawling out from under the table, she is thinking how being a Big Sister is soooo much harder than being a littler one cos you just forget everything when you're smaller. What use are littler brothers at all?

She screws up her face to tie the final knot. She could go back under the table but Daddy just isn't there. Emily thinks her hardest. Outside the sky is blue like always. She still sleeps in her room. Her hair is not orange or brown but yellow like always. But everything is not the same and she doesn't know why. She just knows it makes her Mummy really quiet and not really her same Mummy.

Yesterday Mummy tried to make supper but the custard was all lumps and there hasn't been stories at night neither. It's not her fault. That's Daddy's job. Mummy's is in the City and Daddy's is in the House.

Emily bites her lip hard. She misses her Daddy. There's only one reason she can't find him. He's not here. He mustn't have come back. Her nails are digging into her hands as she thinks it out. The last time she saw Daddy she was sick. In the New Car. She misses her Daddy. Everything changed since Daddy went away.

The door opens again. Emily sees Mummy's legs, knees, tummy, face!

"Emily, come out from under there. I want to-"

Emily does. The minute she is told. Mummy is Talking.

Kate McGrath

# BROKEN

Mummy sits on the couch. Michael, who is following Mummy like a puppy, does too. Emily sits on the floor.

"I need to - There's something -"

Emily waits patiently for Mummy to get going. Her voice probably stopped working when it's not being used. Like Granma's car.

"I don't want you to feel when you're older - convention would suggest that I ought to have told you this sooner -"

Now Mummy is remembering Mummy words. Big long strings of them just like this. You just have to sit and nod and they stop soon enough. Then you can go play. But, Emily thinks, this time she doesn't want to play. She wants her Daddy back.

"Tell Daddy if he comes back I won't be sick anymore."

Mummy changes colour from white to red to white.

Emily wriggles in frustration. Doesn't she know how to use a telephone? Surely they have those not just at Home but in the City too?

Then - Emily wonders if Mummy realises that Emily might just EXPLODE altogether and there would be no more Emily - Mummy starts telling a story NOT answering her question at all!

"A few days ago - a few days ago - Do you remember when we were all in the car a few days ago?"

"You too" says Michael.

"Yes, me too" says Mummy.

"Emily looked all funny."

"Yes, she was sick so we picked her up from her friend's -"

"She gave him my water gun."

"- birthday party. It wasn't your water gun, Michael. We bought it for Trevor's birthday."

"My gun."

"Ok, well the car -"

"Got broke. Daddy got broken too Michael. That's why we all

# BROKEN

went to the hostible."

Mummy looks like Charlie looked when Emily socked the ball into him instead of the net.

Emily continues:

"He didn't come home with us when we were all fixed cos I was sick in the new car and that's what Bold Girls do." Emily feels her face scrunch up.

"Emily, love. It doesn't matter that you were sick - it was an accident. The - the car didn't work right"

"Then bring him back! He must be fixed now!"

"Sometimes people can't be fixed."

My Dad. By Emily.

My Dad is BIG. He wears jumpers wit colours dat Granma buys even tho he don't like dem. My Dad tickles my brudder and he laffs. My Dad plays hide and seek and makes my Mummy smile.

THE DAY MY DAD GOT BROKE I went to smelly Trevor's party cos he's stupid 8. It wasn't fun. My Dad and mummy and michael was going to granma's instead but the bouncy casl is NOT nice and I am sick and Daddy comes to get me and den he pikt me up and I cried in the new car and Mummy pult off my dress so my head went pop and Dad rapped me in a blankie and when we drive I am all sleepy and Dad I wake a bit cos I hear Dad say "How are you doing little one?" and I don't answer cos there's a big noise and the car jumps away from the road. It is driving now not Dad. It did not like the big truk. The big truk scared our car and it jumpt away from the road and Mummy says into a tree. I don't member. I member a crunch and blood, like when you cut your nee but loads more. Mummy reaches back to me and Mikl. He's crying cos he's bleeding from his nose. Mummy asks us if we are ok trying to touch us with her hands. I don't know but I say yes wit my head cos Mummy is crying. Mummy tells Daddy I think they're ok Oisin.

# BROKEN

Daddy is very quiet. His head hurt the window and it is bleeding.

The car came. The big black one that makes Emily feel like Thumbelina. The car makes her shake. It is a bad car. It swallows Emily, Michael and Mummy up and makes Mummy cry. Real tears. Big long sobs. It is a bad, bad car. At least the crows are gone now. Emily was starting to feel cross about having them around again today.

Mummy cried and cried forever in the car. Michael did too cos Mummy was.

Emily looks out the window at a big tree. It's in her head now and she is the big tree. The clouds can cry all they like. They started when Emily came out to the car. The trees never join in. Emily has watched them. The clouds' tears just roll off their leaves.

Kate McGrath

## SEVEN HAIKU

sitting amidst hurrying feet
rain slowly fills
his empty plastic cup

wait till I tell you
the arse fell out of the bucket
it's quite mad

a scent laden trail
buzzing in the sun clad air
pollenmade sweetness

orange berries
metal fence
the bird goes hungry

dark clouds, silent birds,
tingling in the air, raised hairs
the storm is coming

windswept and raincloaked
fury in her eyes and heart
the cailleach rides out

tree skeletons loom
blind stumbling with cold wet feet
fog swallowing sound

Philipp Herrmann

# DUST GHOST

Will I soon be a dust ghost, grey hair upspiked,
grey on my face and nose and lips – grey all over?
Will I shed grey on floors and footpaths,
flowers, leaves that I touch? I am invaded by it.
It creeps around, soundless, shapeless, monster-
amoeba. Grey mist surrounds me.

**I will be a DUST GHOST.**

Críona Ní Gháirbhí

| DÁN | POEM |
| --- | --- |

| soılsíonn | my Star Sleep |
| mo réalc-shuaın | illuminates |
| lámh lasrach | flaming hand |
| míle mıan | thousand desires |
| deoır mheánoíche | midnight tears |
| damhsa cosnochtaıche | barefoot dance |
| mo bhandıa ıstıgh | goddess within me |

Philipp Herrmann & Críona Ní Gháirbhí

# Tommy and Murt

It's morning and Tommy notices how the light seems slow to brighten. A cloudy day, there are no shadows now. He gets up. While waiting for the kettle to boil he looks for a cleaner shirt. He finds one in the corner of the back kitchen and though the buttonholes are wearing wide, he still manages to do each one up with only the tiniest peep of flesh.

Before stepping out the back door he pulls on a knitted blue hat. He likes to feel the morning air on his face. He stands out by the moss covered wall, the stones of which glow luminous lime in the soft grey mist. Sucking in the warmth of the day's first cigarette, he notices how the giant Scots pine appears to breathe as the wind buffets against it. Behind it is the line of beech trees under which he and his brother had played as children. He remembers how they used twigs to shoot at the pigeons that had come to feed on the seeds. At seventy six years old Tommy steps easily in and out of the past. He misses his brother since he went into the nursing home. When he visits, Murt doesn't talk much anymore, in fact he hardly speaks at all.

After his lunch Tommy forces himself to drive down to the village, where he spends an hour or more smoking in his car, the window wound down. He likes to position the old red Fiesta in the square as near to the Spar as he can get it. There he sits and waits for a greeting, a bit of news, some little titbit to bring into his brother. It has taken his neighbours some time to get used to seeing him there.

Lil Donovan is a frequent visitor to the rolled down window. She leans in, warmth on her boozy breath.

"Has Murt settled in yet?" She never waits for a reply. "Tell him Jim had to have the surgery after all, split him open like a mackerel, for all the good it did him. Rotten inside he was."

He has to strain to see her as she steps back to demonstrate the cut.

# TOMMY AND MURT

Tommy hates the medical stuff most of all.

"It'll be wet enough this evening," he replies, looking at the heavy grey in the space behind Lil's curls. He raises his index finger to his cap as another neighbour approaches, and hopes she'll take the hint and go away.

When the rain begins to splatter down Tommy reckons he'll get no more in the village. Before turning the key in the ignition he looks at Murt's accordion which he has placed on the passenger seat. A big brown instrument it has piano like keys instead of buttons. For weeks it has accompanied him on his business and kept silent vigil with him in the village. It is such a dominant instrument in the right hands. The nurses thought it would put too much strain on Murt's back, but tonight Tommy thinks it might be worth the pain.

The rain is heavy as he turns onto the main road. The spray behind the cars appears like smoke. The white vehicle ahead virtually disappears and Tommy has to concentrate more than he feels able to. Coming to a stop inside the car park he notices that the wind has changed direction and now the rain is hitting directly against the windscreen, little bombs of water exploding against the glass before slinking down. No matter what storms there are inside a nursing home, there is no such thing as weather.

As always, every face in the dayroom turns towards Tommy as he walks in. Murt has managed to get his wheelchair as far away from the TV as possible, but it is hard to escape the sound.

Tommy nods to the three critics in the corner who interrupt their game of forty five to wave to him. One of them is Eilis Brown, who was two classes behind him at school. Tommy once thought that he loved her. Now her false teeth have a habit of dropping slightly when she smiles and if he didn't know what a mad cow she was he would have smiled back.

Sandra McTurk

# TOMMY AND MURT

Tommy sees Murt notice the accordion and a ripple break the flatness in his eyes. Gently he lays the instrument in his brother's lap and slips the strap over his arms. Murt sits still for a long time before allowing his hand to slowly stroke the ivory keys of his oldest accordion. His fingers move with great care as he slowly opens the instrument. When he moves the top, it opens like a fan, exposing dark red hidden depths, a slow high note emanates before he reverses it and now the skirt angles out producing another long note. They are muddled sounds and it takes a while before the tune begins to assemble, the pace quickens, and a jig layers upon the notes. Tommy recognises it as, 'The Queen of the Fair.'

Norbu the nurse's aid goes over to turn down the television while one of the critics puts down her hand of cards. Eilis clicks her tongue in exasperation.

Murt moves into 'The Cuckoo's hornpipe', a difficult piece. Tommy can see their father in the furrow of concentration between Murt's eyes and in the tilt of his head as he throws it back. That accordion once belonged to their father. He remembers him playing those same tunes in the kitchen when they were young. At Christmas, some of the neighbours would come in, the whiskey and port wine would be put out along with Tanora for the children. Coloured candles would be lit, white, blue, green and red standing proudly in the turnips hollowed out by Murt and Tommy and decorated with coloured paper bought in Woolworths. Tommy remembers his mother standing clapping at the kitchen door, a blue pinnie on her and she was laughing, tapping her foot to the rhythms of the music. She was always happy, his mother. He tries to catch Murt's eye to see if he remembers it too but his brother's eyes are closed.

Murt's right thumb is bent outwards from the instrument and remains unmoving while the four digits fly across the keys. The muscles around his elbows work like bellows. As Murt leans

# TOMMY AND MURT

backwards it appears as if the weight of the instrument is too much for his frail frame. But just as he appears to topple over, he leans forward with a shift of his shoulders. Two fiery bright red patches appear like slaps on his cheeks. Murt is alive and Tommy knows if he could he would have his right leg moving like the clappers.

Tommy can see that his brother is getting tired and knows he'll only manage one last tune. Murt's brown eyes shine out to his brother. He adjusts the straps before launching into his finale, 'The Battle of Aughrim', and with those sounds, the walls of the nursing home fall flat away and all those listening are transported and can feel the watery wet bogland seeping around their feet. Although they may not know about the causeway and Kilcommodan Hill they can sense the smell of blood, the clash of sharp metal weapons, the stunning blows of canon. The bloodiest battle ever fought on Irish soil. They hear the sad lament of slaughter and lower their heads in grief.

Sandra McTurk

# Death in the Dublin Mountains - Ch 3

"Before we hit the Golf Club let's call in to the home of the Manager first. It's on the way and there is always the element of surprise. They don't expect us to come here. They expect us to go straight to the club."

Kate was not ready for this.

"How do you know the address?"

"I just got the desk sergeant to look it up before we set out. I usually do a bit of foraging around before I leave the station. You never know what you'll find out that could save you later."

"But you said that the Super said that this was really a wild goose chase and not to spend too much time on it."

"Indeed so he did. But we have to start somewhere, and this is on the way."

Kevin looked guilelessly at her.

She didn't know what to make of him. It seemed blindingly obvious to her that a trip to the club, a few brief questions and a quick look around at the site, was all they were expected to do. This looked like time-wasting to her. God, she thought, my very first job and I'm landed with this relic of times past. The lecture of a few short weeks ago came into her head. It was all about efficient modern methods of policing. All about taxpayers' money. And not wasting it.

You're here to learn, she told herself sternly, even if it's only how not to do the job.

They approached the house. It was charming. Every adjective an estate agent ever used could apply here. While she was entranced and stunned and trying to take in all the beauty before her, she heard Kevin say "loads of money".

In time she checked herself from saying, "Have you no soul? How could the first thing you think of be money?"

"Millions, we are looking at millions here", continued Kevin. He could feel a bit of disapproval coming from her. He ignored it.

# DEATH IN THE DUBLIN MOUNTAINS - CH 3

She would have to learn what to look out for. Money was always a factor no matter what you were dealing with.

They continued in silence. The air of tranquillity was disturbed somewhat by a rustle in the flowers. A cat sat and watched a bird. Kate couldn't wait for it to go for the kill. She chased it away.

"Mirzah will be really cross with you my dear. Nature will always win out over nurture you know."

The voice was beautifully modulated. A middle-aged man had come out of the house. The cat came over, arched its back, and wrapped itself around his leg.

"We are making enquiries about the body found locally," said Kevin

"Body? Don't be silly. Whatever gave you that idea? It's some dead animal. I'll bet a local farmer dumped it there when I was abroad." The tone of voice was scornful, then humorous.

"By the way I'm Aubrey O'Hara. I was just returning to the club because I had arranged with your Superintendent to meet you there."

Kevin ignored the message. Loud and clear it was you should not be here. Your superintendent gave you your orders to go to the club.

"Have you noticed anything unusual happening around here recently?"

"No. Nothing at all."

"Anybody else notice anything?"

"Nobody else lives here."

The answer sounded defensive somehow.

"Have you lived here long?"

Kevin had expected a curt answer. But O'Hara seemed to realize that Kevin was getting to ask questions that upset his equilibrium. The answer came in a soft tone of voice.

"I was born here. Some day when you are not busy I would

# DEATH IN THE DUBLIN MOUNTAINS - CH 3

be delighted to show you around. But I know you must go to the so called crime scene," He ended his sentence in a tone of wry amusement.

You are very clever, thought Kevin politely, getting us out of here, but I just have a hunch there is some thing or some body you do not want us to find out about.

O'Hara closed the large oak double door behind him.

"If you follow me I will drive you straight to the golf course."

He had such an air of natural self assurance, that Kevin decided to play along with him and follow his S.U.V. to the site.

# FRANCIS GARY POWERS -THE U2 EPISODE

Francis Gary Powers was a C.I.A. pilot in the late fifties, and veteran with the U.S. Air Force in the Korean War. Later, he engaged in flying numerous C.I.A. spy missions along the Soviet Border. On some occasions, U2 spy planes strayed into Soviet Airspace. Because this was an era before satellite observation, America considered this sort of activity necessary.

On the 1st May 1960, Powers took off from an airbase near Peshawar, Pakistan, in a high altitude U2 surveillance aircraft. He had to fly over the Soviet Union at high altitude to photograph missile sites at Sverdlovsk and Kirov. This very dangerous journey was to take over 9 hours, and cover nearly 4,000 miles. The U.S. planned to fly their spy plane from one end of the Soviet Union to the other for the first time. The mission's planned route was from Peshawar in Pakistan, over the border to the Baikonur Cosmodrome in Kazakhstan, Sverdlovsk, Kirov, Murmansk and then on to safety inside the Norwegian Border at Bodo.

Soviet leader Khrushchev had foreknowledge of the Americans' plans. His air defence systems were waiting - on RED alert. The Soviet Air force fired at the U2 spy plane, near Sverdlovsk, a volley of S.A.M. missiles and not just from one air defence battery. One unarmed Soviet fighter jet was under orders to ram the U2 spy plane. This, according to the Soviet pilot, caught the U2 plane in its slip stream and caused the U2 to flip over and overstress the aircraft. A Soviet Mig 19 was shot down accidentally by one of its own missiles, with the loss of the pilot.

Francis Gary Powers bailed out, fell a few thousand feet, only to find he was unable to free himself from his doomed aircraft. He did not disconnect his oxygen hose. He broke it to free himself. He managed to parachute to safety, but landed down into the hands of the Soviet Authorities. They took him to the Lubianca Prison in Moscow.

The Soviets kept silent for five days. When Powers did not

Patrick Brocklebank

78

# FRANCIS GARY POWERS - THE U2 EPISODE

return, the U.S. information Service in Turkey issued a statement, saying: 'a weather research aircraft had strayed into Soviet Airspace. The pilot had problems with his oxygen equipment and became unconscious, and this violation of Soviet Airspace was not deliberate.'

Premier Khrushchev broke his silence with his announcement that 'an American spy plane had violated Soviet Airspace.' He cunningly did not mention that the pilot was still alive.

The Americans had assumed that Powers was killed. In captivity Francis Gary Powers admitted that he was spying. The U. S. State Department then issued a statement saying: 'Yes, Powers was on an information gathering mission. This had not been authorised by U.S. President Eisenhower.' Then Khrushchev dropped a bombshell saying 'the pilot was alive and well.' Thus he caused considerable embarrassment to the American Government.

Eisenhower then claimed that 'he had approved the mission - it had been necessary to prevent another Pearl Harbour.' After a show trial, Powers was sentenced to a long term in prison in the then Soviet Union. Later, he was exchanged for a Soviet spy held in the U.S.

The incident was just two weeks before an East – West Summit in Paris. The talks collapsed as Eisenhower refused the Soviets an apology. Khrushchev stormed out of the conference. It led to a further deterioration in relations between the two sides.

The C.I.A. did award Powers the highest possible honour, 'The Star of Valour', on his return home. However, they would not allow him to publish his own account of the whole episode till long after the event.

Francis Gary Powers died in a helicopter accident in 1977.

# THE MEMORY RETRIEVER

The world was theirs that day
just the two of them
in a small boat under
a breathless sky.
The hunter watched
his silent hound
balanced on the prow
a figurehead of loyalty
black back glossy
blaze of white on chest
ears tuned below silence
minuscule movements
at the edge of reeds.

They slipped in over
water-sculpted stones
and the dog went crashing
through spent spindle grass
into wetlands.
An explosion of wild duck
in clamorous call
was drowned by his rifle.
The hound retrieved
a twitching bird
in his big, soft mouth.
Later, four more trophies
lay at his feet

Alma Brayden

# THE MEMORY RETRIEVER

emerald heads gleaming
each dun feather faultless
breasts stained red.

As the sun bled
down to darkness
something shuddered
in his perfect world.

Alma Brayden

# She Said

Programmed to your chair
zapped
to the idiot box

pushing buttons
turning yourself on
switching us off

flicking belly fluff
points of view
releasing gases

passing comments
cursing those who choose
to milk the masses

remote, controlled
soap free
empty head

here's a beer, it's warm
chill it with your heart
I'm off to bed

lie there and relapse
there'll be no exertion
for you tonight

Billy Hutchinson

# THE VILLAGE JOINER

Today would be a good day, Jim thought, as he drew open the bedroom curtains. He stood and looked at them, the flower pattern faded in the morning sun. He remembered her years ago, making them, feeding the bright cloth through her new machine. He looked over at her side of the bed. Always up early, my Cath, always busy, making things for me often enough. But today I'm making something for you, something really special.

He opened the workshop door and breathed in. The sharp warm sawdust smell called to him as it did every morning. He lifted a big handful from the pile of dust under the bandsaw, and let it flow softly out through his fingers. It was fresh, only made yesterday, and the resinous scent reminded him of Cath and how she loved to sprinkle sawdust on the fire. Perfumed heat, she called it. Later he would collect some in a bag and bring it indoors. Cath always scolded him if he forgot.

The wood he had cut to size yesterday was waiting on the workbench, and he set to work with his plane, smoothing and shaping. The thin curls forming in front of his careful hands could almost have been Cath's hair, years ago when it was still brown. Jim held up two long shavings and shook them, suddenly remembering her hair leaping in time to the music at a long ago harvest dance.

But really, he thought, her hair was never this colour. She was more a mahogany girl. These are more like our Lily's when she was a little thing, her dark blonde curls covering her tiny head. She'll be glad I'm making this for her Mum. She always asked why Mummy didn't get a wooden toy when I brought her something in from the workshop. Lily didn't notice the chairs, the linen box, the bookshelves. He never had made Cath a toy, although she loved the tiger doorstop he had made after their visit to the zoo on their big anniversary trip. But he made that to please himself, really. To see if he could fix the different colours of wood together to make the stripes.

It worked out pretty well, too, Jim mused. And the kids loved

# THE VILLAGE JOINER

scaring each other with him, and the grandkids. He's well worn, smoothed by so many little hands down the years.

The day passed quickly as Jim worked, almost in a trance as he cut and fixed, dovetailed joints forming under his skilful hands, every detail smooth and perfect, as if it had been there forever. At last his gift was almost finished. He ran his hands gently over the smooth oak. It was warm under his touch, like something alive. He remembered reading that wood never dies, that chopping boards can fight off germs for years. Certainly it can behave like a living thing, he thought, awkward and cussed by times, and at others responding so well, and becoming so beautiful. He gave it another gentle rub with the oiled cloth, and enjoyed its soft sheen, that seemed to glow through the workshop. Only the best was good enough for his Cath, and she would love this. Solid home grown oak, properly seasoned, flat straight boards, none of that twisted quick-dry rubbish. Nor that exotic rubberwood either, whatever the virtues of renewable forests.

Jim went over to the drawers where he kept the cloth, and lifted out a length of white satin. As he did, his mind tumbled back through time, nearly sixty years, and once again Cath was walking towards him up the aisle, her open face laughing in a splendid contrast to the pinched spiritual faces in the row of maiden aunts ensconced in the third pew. Cath was too colourful for them, the poor things. She was nearly too colourful for me at times, Jim grinned to himself, but I got used to her, and what fun we've had. As he worked he let his mind freewheel over the years, enjoying again all the special times he and Cath had had together, smiling to himself, and chuckling once or twice, as his hands moved with the skill of long practice.

At last his work was finished, his creation made. He stood straight and stretched. It was a good piece. The best he could make her. There was only one thing missing now. Bill would collect him tomorrow, and they would take it to Cath, at the hospital. Jim

# THE VILLAGE JOINER

looked back from the door of the workshop, and at last, wiped the back of his hand across his eyes as he threw the switch to plunge the room into darkness.

But the moon was up, and Cath's coffin gleamed in the silky light.

*"Written because my grandfather, A.A. Blackwell, made, to quote my mother then aged 10, 'the best coffins in All England'!"*

Madeline A Stringer

## 28 YEARS

Franz Luginbuehl was annoyed. Glaring down at the slumped figure on his desk he could see the balding spot on the top of the head in the midst of short-cropped, greying hair and the spectacles lying beside it. An insistent beeping noise announced the computers annoyance towards the head resting on the keyboard. The hands clasped the latest report of the Brig-Loetschberg section inventory.

He tried to lift the hand, noticing the prominent blue veins on it. His hand slipped through the flesh and the paper as if they were nothing but smoke. "That's most vexing," he said to himself, "I have to finish that report today so that we can start Month End!"

He heard a cough behind him, somewhat dry and dusty. Franz spun around. "Who are you?" he bellowed.

A tall figure in a black robe looked down at him. "I am Death!" The voice sounded hollow. Franz pulled himself up to his full height – which wasn't very much but made him feel better. "Anybody could say that. Have you got ID?" Sticking out his chest he glared at the tall man, radiating righteous indignation.

"I don't need ID, just look at the scythe and robe!"

"Could have got that from a costume shop."

"How about this then?" barked the dark figure, casting back his hood.

"Nice effect with the glowing eyes, I must admit," Franz said in a level voice.

"How did you get that mask on?"

"See for yourself. Try taking it off," Death suggested.

Franz's hands moved around the skull, over the sides where the ears would have been and lastly to the back.

"Oh" said Franz Luginbuehl.

"Now that we have that over with," Death sighed, "Franz Luginbuehl, you are dead! See that there on the desk? That's your body." He looked at Franz expectantly.

"How do I get back in then?"

Death's eyes flickered red for a moment. "What do you mean, back in?"

"I haven't finished the inventory yet, see, and Month End is

# 28 YEARS

coming up. Management accounts can't start their Month End without the inventory report complete and they will be upon me like a ton of bricks. And then we have the auditors coming next month; you have no idea what they are like. They rip you apart if you're not prepared. And with that waster Dobmann out sick we are down one man."

"This is all behind you now, Franz. Time to pass over."

"Listen, this is really most inconvenient. Could you come back another time? You can't expect me to drop everything just because you're Death? I'd need more notice than that. Tell you what, you make an appointment with my secretary and I'll see if I can fit you in."

"I don't make appointments, I appear at the right time."

"Well, this isn't it! And besides it's terribly rude to appear without an appointment."

"It's time to go now!"

"Says who? Listen, it's too early, I've got too much to do." His brows furrowed. "Here, the average life span of a male Western European is 79, and I am 51. So that gives me another 28 years. Help me get back in!"

"You are not average! The time is now, come on!"

"Are you saying I am below average? "Red veins pulsed in Franz's neck, his little fat hands pressed into his hips, elbows out. "First you come in here without any appointment, drag me out of my body and tell me that I am dead. And now you insult me! Get out of here now before I call security!" The boiling rage within the little man threatened to push the eyes out of his head. His face turned red and his body tensed, ready to start jumping up and down on a moment's notice.

"You have no say in that. Your life has ended."

"Yeah right, that's what you say! You can't just come in and boss me around! Get me back into my body this instant!"

"You can't go back, it's already going into rigor mortis."

"Rigor mortgage my foot! Get me back or I'll complain to your supervisor! I have 28 years left and you won't take them from me!"

Philipp Herrmann

# 28 YEARS

"Come with me, now!" Death moved forward to grip Franz's wrist.

"28 years! Ha! I've been working in this place longer that!"

Death's skeletal fingers now wrapped around Franz's wrist. The small man wriggled and pulled for a moment but there was no use. Death's grip was like a vice. Then Franz's face softened and broke into a sly grin.

"Wait, I have to get my lunch out of the fridge." He nodded at the little box beside the desk.

"There's no time!" Death almost wailed now.

"Last request, remember? You're honour bound to grant it!"

"That's executions. I generally come in after."

"Well, think of it as a new experience."

"Very well, then. After that you come with me. No more discussion."

Death released his grip and the little man darted for the door. He rushed through and slammed it shut, turning the key. He leaned heavily against it, taking in a big gulp of air.

"What in the name of sanity is this?"

Eyes wide he took in the scene before him. There was his desk and on it his body, slumped over the keyboard.

"The door out of my office opens into it. That's ridiculous!"

"ENOUGH!" Death roared. "I tried the nice approach but it doesn't seem to work with you." Death approached, scythe swinging, eyes blazing in a furious blue.

"Here listen, put that thing down or I'll call the police. This is downright dangerous, swinging something like that in a small space. You'll break something."

Retreating, Franz hit the wall with his back. He tried to squash himself into a corner and then curled up into a ball. A small wimper emerged from it.

Death towered above him, scythe raised. In a swooshing arc he cleanly cut Franz's soul cord. As the spectre of Franz Luginbuehl faded away a thin whisper could be heard. "28 years! I had 28 years left! You cheat!"

Philipp Herrmann

# THURSDAY MORNING 4AM

Angel breath upon my neck
As I gently carry
My human time-bomb
To his resting place for now.

Two winks later big sister arrives for comfort
Cold feet against my leg, wide awake,
Thirsty, chatty, says 'I love you'
Put arm around, and my snores begin.

Last night's aria now forgotten
Only red eyes and fuzzy head
To show the world my love
My sleep soon to return, I hope.

Joe McNally

## DOORMATS

Any chance of a lazy Sunday afternoon in front of the fire reading the newspapers is blown away when my daughter announces that she has to have new trainers today. Not tomorrow. Not yesterday but now.

As far as I am concerned going into a sports shop to buy a teenager trainers is like lowering myself into a pit of burning tar. It's all to do with the heaving dance music pouring out from screens on every wall, the completely indifferent, under-trained, under-paid teenage staff, and the mogadon headed customers whose screaming toddlers should be running around the park not sitting strapped into buggies. But I'm there now and I decide to make the best of it. We both stand slack-jawed, blankly gazing at the altar of Reebok, Nike and Adidas. The white branded beacons of pure unadulterated consumerism sit on their individual stands signalling 'buy me, buy me, buy me' to adolescent brains.

I try, I really do try, to work out why one pair of trainers is 130 and the other is 30. I pick one up and then the other. Same brand, same material, same sole. Different coloured stripe on the side. A different coloured stripe costs 100. But I am too long in the tooth to say this out loud. Oh no I will be accused of not understanding anything.

Eventually, one of the indifferent staff sidles up. A Justin Bieber clone in fact. His long fringe hiding his sleepy eyes. "OK?" It's not so much a question that he asks us but a pathetic bleat that begs us not to ask for anything that may require him to actually do anything. My daughter stares at the ground and her shoulders move upwards. I point to the pair of 30 trainers. "They're nice?" I venture. "Mum, they're disgusting," she whispers. "Well I don't see what's so bad about them." I say a bit sniffily. "You just like them because they're cheap." I swear teenagers can read a parent's mind without even trying. "What about these?" at 60 they are at my secret maximum spend. No comment from my daughter.

Eileen Counihan

# DOORMATS

Justin Bieber is moving away. I can feel my palms sweat. If he goes, he will disappear behind the staff door never to re-emerge in my lifetime. We will be left wandering in this noisy hellhole for ever. I take the plunge. "Have you got these in size 6?" He trudges off to look reluctantly.

While we wait, I exchange glances with other victims. One particular paragon of maternal virtue catches my eye. She is carrying two pairs of football boots back to her eight year old David Beckham. She holds up the offerings for his approval. He glances at the boots with all the expertise of a diamond assayer, "Yes" he says perumptorily, pointing to one pair, "they can go in the 'maybe' pile. The other pair are a definite no." The 'maybe' pile has about twelve pairs stacked up neatly. I look back at the mother who is already obediently returning the 'no' pair to the shelf. I consider asking her if she is on drugs or has she undergone frontal lobe lobotomy that ensures she never questions or argues with her offspring but patiently waits for his next order? I want to whisper words of encouragement and emancipation to this obviously broken woman.

But my daughter catches my eye with a warning glance. "Maybe" she says quietly "I can wear my old pair for the next while." A reprieve. We escape before Justin comes back and buy two hot chocolates on the way home.

Eileen Counihan

# 19 AND 15

Nearly six foot of gangle
gets into bed beside me,
and a beautiful woman
brings her duvet and sits on my feet,
and once again a Christmas morning
resounds with laughter
and "look at this!" and "what is it?"
and I sink below another sea of tissue paper.
An unbroken line of chocolate coins
and a-mandarin-in-the-toe
seems to stretch back through the years
to when they were soft bundles
drowsing milkily against my neck.
But before the past can become more
than a prickle in my eyes,
comes "look at my bubbles!"
and "would you like a marshmallow?"
and the solid happy presence of them
breaks the spell,
and I think, -despite all troubles,
mistakes and failures,
to have raised such kids as these
I have done well.

Madeline A Stringer

## AFTER THE STORM

The much celebrated Spring,
so full of promise and bloom,
decimated -
and after such a long Winter too.
The storm predictors
scoffed at and scotched
by the tenders of the crops;
seeds nurtured for harvesting
scattered like some migrant flock
to better climes;
edifices still teetering in the aftershock
slowly, slowly, being rebuilt
under careful supervision;
longer days
casting new light on old ways -
Summer may bring some remission
but hardly enough;
the hoped-for harvest
still a long, long, way off.

Phil Lynch

## ROAD TRIP

As their wagon crested the final hill onto the open expanse of the brief summit, William could see that the town of Wisdom, Missouri, was very different to how it had appeared in his dreams. It was certainly nothing like he had expected as they steadily worked their way down to the large conflagration of buildings and activity by the river. Buildings were buildings but the river was mesmerising, bigger and wider than anything he had ever seen. Putting his hand on his brow to shade his eyes from the late afternoon sun, he could see the various barges and river boats. Some were two or three deep lined up against the dock, and the town expanded out like a balloon from this southern shore. In the centre of town, an iron crucifix bestrode the spire of the church. Easily the tallest building in town, he knew from talking with Ned that it was right in the centre and so was the landmark for every direction. If he got lost or detached during the trip all he needed to know was his way back from there and he would be fine.

Apart from the occasional night out under the stars when he and Billy Ray Pickford, Preacher Pickford's son, had been let off to practice being cowboys - by far their favourite childhood pastime - William had never spent a night under any other roof than God's or his own in all his twelve years. Tonight that was going to change. Pappy and Ned always stayed at Peggy's Place the night before market. Last night before they left the plantation, William had heard his Momma talking to Pappy about the sleeping arrangements for the following night: "...and you make sure William has a comfortable bed now..." It was sealed. He could almost feel the weight of the woollen blankets of the strange bed across his chest, him lying by the wall and Pappy in the bed by the window. He fell asleep dreaming about all of the sounds that he would be hearing through the door, wall, and floorboards from the hotel corridor and beyond.

There was no gradual entry to Wisdom. One moment they

# ROAD TRIP

were on the dusty road into town, and a turn of the wagon wheels later they were in the street. William had never been in such a big place before. Sure, he had gone to Henderson a few times as a child with Momma, but that was only to the General Store to get some new britches or to get him out from under Pappy's feet if he was particularly busy with new stock or whatever. Heck knows there was nothing else there but it, the saloon, the blacksmiths, a barber shop and four houses scattered opposite. No more than a fifty yard gap in the prairie.

This was much different. His eyes darted from saloon, to store, to the hotel on the corner, hoping to see Peggy's name on the sign. After a ways they passed the Sherriff's office. Almost directly across the street was the 'Wisdom Gun Store estd. 1845'. He had no idea what 'estd' meant and knew not to ask but smiled at its location. Maybe it was there first and the law office joined later or maybe it was the other way round. Either way he knew that business was never going to be as brisk as it could have been if it were in another part of the town.

Up ahead he saw a store selling ladies' clothing. Maybe he would have time to visit it to try and get something nice for Momma; some fabric for a new dress or even just enough for a bonnet, something the womenfolk round home would never have seen before. He'd been saving since as long as he could remember and had brought most of it with him in the hope of such an opportunity. He pictured her going to church in her new outfit. All the looks, nudges and elbows among the other ladies of the congregation as she walked through the oak door and down the aisle of the church arm in arm with Pappy, William beaming as he followed respectfully a few feet behind, enjoying their awe. Momma would be so cheered by the attention and especially in telling all who wanted to know that "... my William got this for me last time he was in Wisdom". Her chest full to bursting as she received their acclaim for what a good boy

# ROAD TRIP

her son was and how they only wished that theirs were as good to them. In his mind's eye he could see it all and the envious looks from her neighbours as they walked back to their wagons for the journey home. Dressed in the same Sunday best that they had worn for years and ruminating the chidings that were going to be handed out over the dinner table that evening.

William had never seen such diversity on God's good earth before, nor known that, all this time, it had existed less than a whole day's journey from home. He stared almost slack-jawed as their wagon slowly wound its way through the streets towards the livery stable which Ned had told him was at the far end of town. All shapes and sizes walked the boarded sidewalks in everything from the simplest to the most garish wardrobes. Most every side street was populated by streams of steam and clouds of Coolies going about their daily laundry grind. There were horses everywhere, carrying or pulling the general populous on their daily business. The majority of them were reined in front of some type of wagon or other. The remainder carried a heady mix of character. Most were men in their woollen day suits and bowler hats, clearly not men of the land, locals to a man.

As they approached the church he caught the eye of a young man, no more than early twenties, waiting by the side of a house. He was slouching in his saddle as if waiting for something to happen. William thought him easily the gunfighter type. His cheap clothes, worn boots and battered hat were betrayed by his gun all shiny and prominently positioned in its black leather holster, slightly cocked due to the position of his stirruped right leg. His right hand rested on the pommel holding the reins, his left down by his side. The stranger smiled at him, tipping the brim of his hat with his free left hand as he did so. Almost in acknowledgement of reading the boys mind, he deliberately cast open the right side of his jacket to afford William a better look at the weapon, trying his best to keep

# ROAD TRIP

the 'see what I got' look from his youthful face. On sight, William knew it was a .45, your archetypal six-shooter and the favoured gun of those in the shooting trade. He smiled in return and nodded his head in thanks to his new acquaintance and watched him disappear into the fabric of the town as they journeyed on.

After a few more minutes of looking in wonder at everything he could see, he felt the horses slow to a sedate but bouncy trot as Pappy pulled in on the reins. They knew where they were. Up ahead, the large wooden doors of the livery were open wide into the barn. As they approached, William could see stalls on either side and, straight through, a large dirt paddock out back. Through the white rimmed square window positioned top centre above the entrance he could see the golden glow of a mass of hay and straw. Either side of the window were the words 'Wisdom' and 'Livery'. They had arrived.

William bubbled with excitement at the prospect of the evening ahead and the market tomorrow, and had to restrain himself not to jump off the wagon with a whoop. Pappy had a strict rule about showing emotion. Such behaviour was only for the heathen, not for a true God fearing man whose duty it was to remain modest at all times and show respect for the Creator.

Within a matter of minutes they had parked the wagon out back, unhitched the horses and given their reins to the stable hand to bring them for a drink and some feed. Gathering their belongings, they made their way on to the street and paused. Finally able to take his time and fill his lungs with the heady air of the town, he could feel his vitals rising and the spirit of excitement course through his young veins. Only William carried anything. Pappy expected him to carry his travel kit in addition to his own small bag. Thankfully Ned had decided to wear his suitcase.

"How's about we go get some vittels Ned?" said Pappy.

"Sounds good to me Mr. Lorimer. Wonder what Peggy's got

# ROAD TRIP

cooking tonight?" replied Ned.

William tried hard to keep up with the pace of the two men from livery to hotel and by the time they reached their destination some hundred yards later, was about fifteen feet behind. A non-descript building situated on a corner; Peggy's had an array of windows stretching four wide on either side of the swing-door entrance. At three stories, it was one higher than the other buildings on the street and William prickled at the thought of possibly sleeping so high up, directly under the painted red roof with the white 'Peggy's' emblazoned for all to see. His first view inside was shadowed by Ned smirking back at him as the force of the opened doors swung back shoulder high, knocking off his hat. 'God damn Ned!' he cursed to himself, dropping both bags to the ground to gather it up. He struck it against his leg to clean the dust from the rim, before placing it firmly back in place.

Walking from the sidewalk decking onto the polished wooden floor, his heart skipped a beat. He'd never even seen a place like it before. Let alone actually stayed the night in one. By the large wooden desk, talking with a smiling Pappy, stood what could only be Peggy. A short round woman of about fifty, William thought. Somewhat overly dressed for the time of day, she wore a purple velvety dress with black lace down the sides and a plunge of flesh straight down from her neck, over ample bosom, to somewhere just above her navel. William couldn't help smiling too.

## STUDYING BIOLOGY

I admit it, I'm a nervous animal. Here I am going into the library to sit with all the other Leaving Certificate students and there she is, Jessica O'Connor from Sion Hill. With her long blonde hair cutting her face in half and her pink bag at her feet, totally immersed in her study. My heart is doing a flip and I feel eyes on me as I cross the room. Of course no-one is looking at me, but nonetheless I feel like a TV screen.

Amazingly, there's a free space beside her. Should I sit so close? Looks like I've no choice, it's the last seat. I sit down as quietly as I can and dig into my bag. The chair gives a squeal and I freeze, sensing a movement to my right. She's glanced up and is looking my way. I turn my head as if by accident, and as I bring out a book and a pen I see she's smiling at me. Feck, Jessica O'Connor is smiling at me! I wonder what she'd think if she found out I really sat my Leaving Cert last year?

Billy Hutchinson

# MELLIFONT ABBEY

The glade is loud with the zeal of bees.
No doubt disturbs their dogmatic drone.
They fumble inside auricular lilies
drunk on summer's insistent song.
The cellular mind is ignorant
how Nature finds the comb unshaped
and in its wax a lattice stamps.
Habit, the extent of apian faith.

Inside the hive's monastic order
what impulse fires the royal alembics
that gild its buff prismatic chambers?
What hex refined this cloying amber?
Dear God, could sightless petals mix
the hectic hues, to goad such ardour?

Dave Butler

# The Turner Exhibition

Solstice-works
preserved in darkness,
breaking through
mid-winter's clutch
to hang as jewels
on the walls.
We, the pupils of his eyes
follow his fixation
with luminous clouds
laid in layers
of diffused light.

In Venice he had two skies
the second, a reflection
in lazulite water
washed on ragtag paper
or pigment onto linen.
He stalked the sun along
its path and caught it
with its cloud-guard down,
sometimes, behind Salome's veil
before it danced below the rim
of dimming earth.

Alma Brayden

# A DAY LESS ORDINARY

It had rained most of the night. The constant drip-drip-drip from the leaking gutter had kept him awake. Bleary-eyed and short of temper, O'Brien mumbled as he searched for his keys. "Where the hell has she put them?" They were on the mantelpiece where he had left them. "I'll fix that bloody gutter later!" he grumbled and left by the front door.

The morning sun raised small plumes of vapour from the grey footpath, but it could do little to lift his spirits. Before crossing the road he unwrapped a mint he had produced from his pocket, and a small dog appeared at his side.

"Die for your country, Rebel!" and the little fellow rolled on his back, kicking his short legs. "Ah but can ye recite the Foggy Dew?"

"Those things can't be good for you," he told the little mutt as he tossed the mint into its mouth.

On the other side of the road he cursed as he stepped into a puddle, splashing his highly polished shoes.

Emerging from the corner shop with his paper rolled tightly under his arm, O'Brien strode along the familiar street towards the bus stop. His pace quickened upon checking his watch, and he had to run the last few yards to hop onto the back of the departing bus.

"A very good morning to you, Mr. O'Brien," greeted the conductor. "Will it be your usual seat by the window sir?"

"That will do nicely Tom. Thank you."

His usual seat by the window had been taken by a lady with a rather oversized hat. The driver crunched a new gear as O'Brien settled with a bump into the seat beside her. She smiled politely from beneath her floral magnificence and he acknowledged her presence with a nod.

Opening the neatly rolled newspaper, he remembered the carefully folded bolts of cloth in his father's shop. He spread his fingers on his lap and recalled the smooth fabrics which would be spread out before his father's skilled scissors.

Anthony O'Farrell

# A Day Less Ordinary

"Double smooth for the quality," his father would say. "We'll make something special out of that... And you my boy, we'll make something special out of you!"

Always happy with his life as a tailor, the old man had enjoyed the "dailyalities of life" as he called it.

"And how are things in the world of high finance?" enquired the conductor, as he expertly produced a ticket from the machine, which swung on the worn leather strap around his neck. The man accepted the fare, and gave the correct change, all the while balancing legs apart, like a gun-fighter in the OK Corral.

"Never a dull moment, Tom!"

"All that high-falutin' ticking and totting. I ask ya!"

"You're not wrong, Tom," said O'Brien with a sigh.

"Bourke and Associates, Good Morning," said Miss Healy in her best telephone voice.

"You're late, O'Brien," said Mr. Bourke.

"Its five minutes to, by my reckoning sir," protested O'Brien.

The older man turned to face him. An oily lick of his thinning hair swung loose and his stale cigarette breath assaulted O'Brien's face.

"I'll put you through now sir," said Miss Healy.

"I'll take it in my office. And it is Bourke and Associates Chartered Accountants, Miss Healy. How many times must I tell you? This firm has a reputation to uphold!"

Miss Healy adjusted her seat with a wiggle of her hips and as Mr. Bourke shut the door behind him, she stuck out her tongue.

"Well good morning to you, Mr. O'Brien," she said.

"He'll catch you doing that one day," warned O'Brien.

The phone rang again.

"Bourke and Company Chartered... Oh Eileen, how are you?"

O'Brien crossed the room to his desk and removed his jacket,

# A Day Less Ordinary

before returning to the reception to gather the morning post. As office manager it was his duty to sort the mail every day. He had authority to open all letters addressed to the company, but anything addressed to Mr. Bourke was to be left at the desk unopened.

"Oh I know Eileen, they are so expensive..."

"Careful," whispered O'Brien, and gestured to his employer's door. "He'll be out any minute."

"But don't you think red is my colour, Eileen? No darling, heels can never be too high!"

She stretched herself easily on her office chair and let her long legs glide from under her desk, to point and wriggle her toes playfully at O'Brien.

"I wish you wouldn't do that, Miss Healy!"

"Oh sorry Eileen, it's my boss. No not him, the good-looking one."

Mr. Bourke's door opened.

"Have to go Eileen, bye!" and she hung up the phone.

"Mr. Bourke, may I have a word with you please?" asked O'Brien.

"If it's about that promotion again, I've already told you, you're not qualified!"

"It's not that, sir."

"Well, what is it then?"

"It's a personal matter, sir."

"Oh for God's sake. Not now man, later!"

"Yes sir."

O'Brien spent the rest of his working morning reconciling a client's bank account, ticking each transaction on the bank statement against the corresponding entry in the relevant cash book, and carefully totting the totals.

He had no appetite for lunch, opting instead for a short walk

# A Day Less Ordinary

along the canal bank.

He sat in the sun for a while and stared into the black water. Reflections twisted and distorted on the surface, mirroring passing shoppers, and a small boy holding his father's hand. He squinted against the glare and used a neatly folded handkerchief to dab beads of perspiration from his brow. A lorry's engine, knocking somewhere on the busy road behind him, disturbed his thoughts and he left.

Back at his desk at five minutes before the hour, O'Brien began again his weary task of ticking and totting, ticking and totting. Miss Healy was at her desk, filing her nails and sucking on the mint that O'Brien had given her. The intercom buzzed.

"Yes Mr. Bourke?" she answered.

"You may tell Mr. O'Brien that I will see him now."

"Yes, Mr. Bourke."

O'Brien was already on his feet.

"His Lordship will see you now."

Bourke's office was untidy. Files and loose papers lay scattered across his desk. Boxes stuffed with bills and receipts overflowed on the floor. Working papers, ledgers everywhere, all manner of paperwork and correspondence tied together with string.

O'Brien waited. Bourke did not look up.

"Sit."

O'Brien obeyed.

"I have here a letter from Corrigan Solicitors..."

"I need some time off, sir."

"Listen to me, O'Brien. This is a very grave matter, a very grave matter indeed. Mr. Corrigan claims there are funds missing from his client account."

"Two weeks would be plenty sir..."

Anthony O'Farrell

# A DAY LESS ORDINARY

"What are you talking about? Have you not heard what I said? Corrigan has discovered missing funds from his client account!" reiterated Mr. Bourke.

"You see, sir, Mrs. O'Brien is unwell…"

"Don't be absurd, man!" shouted Bourke. "Corrigan claims to have discovered misappropriation! We signed his accounts, gave him a clean audit report. He is threatening to bring the matter to the attention of the institute! Consider the damage. Our reputation will be ruined. My grandfather set up this business, O'Brien…"

"Yes sir, in 1905."

"Exactly, and in three generations there has never been as much as a hint of…of impropriety! This firm is built on our reputation. The reputation of my father, and his father before him."

"May I have the time off, sir?"

"What? No sir, you may not!" shouted Bourke.

O'Brien watched the angry man, his mouth spitting, his mind tearing.

"What's wrong with you, O'Brien? We signed that audit report…! If there is anything…"

"You signed the audit report, sir," O'Brien said coldly.

"What did you say?"

"You signed it, sir. I'm not qualified… remember?"

Bourke's rigid body seemed to almost collapse in shock. His shoulders slumped and his face changed from angry red to sickly grey. O'Brien looked on, his face impassive, content in the knowledge that the other man was watching his precious reputation bleed away.

After a long silence Bourke spoke.

"What do you know about this, O'Brien?"

O'Brien did not answer. He looked at Bourke through empty eyes. Then stood up and walked out of the office.

Anthony O'Farrell

# A Day Less Ordinary

"Time gentlemen please. Have ye no homes to go to?" O'Brien looked at his watch. Almost mid-night. His mind was suddenly clear as if he had stepped down or moved away from something. Whatever it was, it had ended.

He swallowed what remained of the bitter brew in his glass, and wiped his mouth with the back of his hand. O'Brien realised that he had no real memory of the events of the afternoon. Only the images remained in his mind, like slices of time.

"Jesus!" he thought. "I must have drunk myself sober."

He put down the empty glass and left the pub.

The mid-night streets were quiet as he walked the short distance to his home. Ahead of him, a man walked hand in hand with a small boy. He had seen them earlier, on the canal bank. The boy kept turning and looking over his shoulder, but was too far away for O'Brien to make out his face.

Before turning the key to his front door, he watched their silhouettes fading into the blue black night.

"I'm home dear," he called and closed the door behind him.

O'Brien entered the small living room and sat down on the sofa beside his wife.

Her three day old corpse slid to one side. Her head pivoted grotesquely. O'Brien's dressing-gown cord was still wrapped around her broken neck.

The constant drip-drip-drip from the leaking gutter would keep him awake.

Anthony O'Farrell

# BUTTERFLIES HAVE WINGS

They say God never sends a hurt
Unless we have the strength
To see the value through the dirt,
To live life's bitter length.

The lesser only know today
They fly or dive or run
We know that we will have to pay
For every type of fun.

The lonely polar on his floe
Is simply trying to fish.
But we are cursed because we know
Life will evade our wish.

We know the end will come too fast
We won't have seen life flee
We watch the future and the past
But most forget to be.

Aware of moment, life is long,
Our dogs and cats are free
Of fear or needing to be strong
For when they cease to be.

We struggle and we try to cope,
Even the cricket sings
We humans have to live by hope
But butterflies have wings.

Madeline A Stringer

## SEASONINGS

Every day I see the sea
and every day it changes
every day reminding me
how nature rearranges.

Every season changes colour
and every season fashions
every season leaves me fuller
of nature's newest passions.

Every bud that gently grows
and every bud so tender
every bud its centre shows
as Spring unveils its splendour.

Every bird that soars on high
and every bird retracing
every bird sings songs of joy
to Summer's warm embracing.

Every leaf begins to fade
and every leaf is falling
every leaf to earth degrade
it's Autumn's nature calling.

Every time I see it snow
and every time it freezes
every time I feel the blow
of Winter's icy breezes.

Every thing a reason gives
and every thing a meaning
every thing that grows and lives
gives reason to our weaning.

Phil Lynch

# HANDPRINT

life's painted tale
in ink blue lines
in ochre spots
in stiffened joints
in scars showing
turning points

Philipp Herrmann

# FARCE IN ALL SENSES

### "Caroline" at the Mill Theatre
*Dermot Pomeroy, Irish Times*
This new writer on the Irish stage has a long way to go before her work can be counted amongst the Masters of Irish Theatre. She is no John B Keane, no Marina Carr, certainly no Oscar Wilde. Sally Jones, God help her, is not even a poor man's Brian Rix.

An uneven cast did their best to rescue this amateur writing from the abyss of unbelievability, and almost succeeded. We were let down by a piece of absurd casting which put a young lady of more than average avoirdupois in the eponymous lead role, and after we had laughed once, uncomfortably, at her difficulty in negotiating the many doors of this over-complex set, the joke wore thin and the director had to fall back on the extremely weak writing. Manus O'Driochta has directed better, and more competently. His Nicholas Nickleby in the Gate last year was superb, so we know he can pull a tour de force out of a masterpiece and can only conclude that it is true that a silk purse cannot be made from a sow's ear. Much of the vernacular in this piece would sit most comfortably with the sow, and did not help the action, though there was much uneasy laughter on Saturday night.

I hope this young cast will soon find another showcase for their developing talents so that we may be allowed to judge them for themselves.

### Laughter all the way - "Caroline" at the Mill Theatre.
*Erica Ni Shuillabhain, Irish Trumpet*
The Mill Theatre in Dundrum was the setting for a great laugh last Saturday night when a new comedy, 'Caroline', opened. We were all sore in the ribs by the time it ended, and Sally Jones the author was called onto the stage to take a standing ovation by the enthusiastic audience. She was obviously delighted with the success of her hilarious play, and we all hope she will write many more.

Madeline A Stringer

# FARCE IN ALL SENSES

'Caroline', the heroine, was played by Molly Brownlow, who was very funny as she raced around the stage, trying to find out if her husband really was up to no good. The jokes came thick and fast and we really needed the interval to recover. The second half was just as funny, - and I won't tell you the surprise ending. You have to go and see it for yourselves. You won't regret it.

**Other news**
*St. Edmond's Parish Newsletter*
We are sorry we cannot bring you a review of the play which is now running in the Mill Theatre, which was written by Sally Jones, one of our parishioners. You will remember Sally from the fete in June, when she delighted the children with a guess-how-many-sweets-in-the-bottle, filled with her own homemade fudge and toffees. She tells us there were 117. Our usual theatre reviewer, Esmé Millar, is laid up with a bad sore throat, and her usual replacement, Aoibheann Smith, is only 17 so could not attend the play.

Those of you who are prepared to risk an over-18s show must judge it for yourselves!

We wish Sally all the best with her play, but hope her new venture will not stop her making her delicious fudge!

**Theatre Reviews**
*Travel Freebie - the quality paper for Dublin's commuters*
A hilarious comedy by a Dublin writer opened last night in the Millstone theatre in Dundrum. 'Chairlift' had everyone rolling in the aisles as Milly Brown, the heroine, rushed around after her husband. It is extremely funny and has a surprise ending. Not to be missed. ★ ★ ★ ★ ★

## AFTERMATH

Found his brother's shoes. Held them up to show no-one. Knee-deep in mud that had been somewhere else only 15 minutes earlier. A rescuer had draped a plastic sheet around him. He didn't know why. But left it there for fear of offending. Felt frozen in time while the men in brown covered green overalls, ran around shouting. Sound made no impression. There were no echoes. People stood close by, heads down, quiet. Grey streaked pink walls bounded him and a torch light lit his face for what seemed like forever. No longer recognised his house. For this moment his clock had stopped. Colourless tree trunks lay where once his parents had slept.

Billy Hutchinson

# RECOVERY

Black clouds boiled over the sky.
Rain raked the grass, curled along the roofs.
Afternoon coughed into night.
His world had been cycloned by a snarling mouth.
Doglike he sniffed the dawn,
Leaned into the silvery morning.

Maggie Gleeson

# BELOW ZERO

The days of summer stretch beyond the frame
Yet still, my memory struggles on to dwell
In places that pretend to stay the same:
Beside a lake where light and sound excel,
Where thrush's song continues on and on.
Now, callous winter brings a silence there,
All water-coloured geese and swans are gone.
Shroud snow has come to bind up everywhere.
Frost draws its abstract etchings on the glass,
Cold, marbled path of walkers lies bereft.
The dreams I dreamed have failed to come to pass,
Dry memories of skeletons are left.
Soon, time will come when spring and winter meet
To change the wind to whisper warm and sweet.

Alma Brayden

## WAVE WATCHING

The water is shot silk,
waves leap over each other
jostle to the shore
their rhythmic drum
the heartbeat of the sea.
Gulls settle and rise
settle and rise.

One wave gathers itself
pulls in froth of surf
gives a wide green yawn
curves in
turns ink blue
streals of russet tresses
lie on its smooth curl.

A white feather
dances on the cusp
catching brightness
rushing water brings it in
leaves it stranded, sanded,
pulls it out, still dancing;
a sky-gift from a gull.

Alma Brayden

## MEET THE AUTHORS

### ANTHONY O'FARRELL

Anthony joined Dalkey Writers' Workshop in 2007. He has written a number of plays for the stage and radio, as well as short stories for adults and children. His first novel 'Suvla' has recently been published in e-book format.

### ALMA BRAYDEN

Alma is a poet, visual artist and member of Dalkey Writers' Workshop. Her first collection was published by 7 Towers in May 2010. Her work has appeared in many anthologies, literary magazines, CDs and, DVDs. She teaches art and has had many exhibitions.

### BILLY HUTCHINSON

Billy has run his own graphic design business for twenty years. He lives in Dublin, and joined Dalkey Writers' Workshop in 2004. He is currently working on a novel, and continues to produce flash fiction, short stories and poetry.

### MADELINE ANN STRINGER

Madeline has been playing with writing for aeons - winning a prize from the Puffin Club back in the mists of time - but has only been able to put serious effort into it recently. Her "Rhyme for Reason" was awarded a merit certificate for the writing in the Bray One-Act Festival. It and 'Two Wrongs' also appeared on the 'All-Ireland Festivals' in '09 and '10. She has also written two novels.

## MEET THE AUTHORS

### MAGGIE GLEESON

Maggie is a founder member of the Dalkey Writers' Workshop. She has had her comedy broadcast by RTE, and has written scripts for award-winning television documentaries.

### CRÍONA NÍ GHÁIRBHÍ

Críona, born in West Clare, now lives in Dublin. She writes as Gaeilge and in English and has read her poetry on four continents including in Ireland. Her poems have been published in Ireland and in Britain. In 2003, she founded Dalkey Writers' Workshop and chaired it for many years. Críona also founded Deansgrange Writers' Workshop.

### JOE MCNALLY

A native of Glenasmole in the Dublin mountains, Joe has been writing for many years and is currently working on his first novel. A member of Dalkey Writers' Workshop since 2010, he has since branched out into poetry and shorter prose pieces themed primarily around his two children and the quirkier side of life.

### EILEEN COUNIHAN

Eileen joined the Dalkey Writers' Workshop in Spring 2010. She writes short stories and was runner-up in the 2007 Francis McManus Radio Short Story awards and winner of the 2008 Listowel Writers' Week, Bryan McMahon short story award. Her work has also appeared in other short story anthologies. She is currently working on a short story collection.

# MEET THE AUTHORS

### PHILIPP HERRMANN

Originally from Switzerland, Philipp has been living in Ireland since 2001 and has been a member of Dalkey Writers' Workshop since October 2009. He writes both poetry and prose and loves experimenting with words.

### MARY HANLON

Mary has been a member of the Dalkey Writers' Workshop since its inaugural meeting. She has produced and directed plays for teenagers, one of which reached the finals of a competition and was staged in the Gate Theatre. She has written short stories, completed a crime novel and is currently working on her second.

### SANDRA McTURK

Sandra graduated from N.C.A.D. and worked for many years in the visual arts. She enjoys making pictures with words and is particularly interested in writing short stories. She was selected as the overall winner of the beginners section of Ireland's Own Original Writing Competition. She has also been short listed in the Molly Keane Memorial Creative Writing Award.

### DAVE BUTLER

Dave's novel *The Last European* was published in 2005 and his poetry collection *Via Crucis* in 2011. His poetry awards include the Ted McNulty, Brendan Kennelly and Feile Filiochta International, and his short stories have twice won the Maria Edgeworth Award.

# MEET THE AUTHORS

### ANDREW FURLONG

Andrew endeavours to assist fellow writers in the Dalkey Writers' Workshop, which he joined in 2005, with constructive criticism, and is grateful for their many excellent suggestions on how to develop his own writing skills and craft. He wrote *Tried for Heresy A 21st Century Journey of Faith* (2003). His website promotes human rights and discusses theological concerns. He works as Secretary General of the FairFund Federation. He lives in Dalkey.

### KATE MCGRATH

Kate lives in Dun Laoghaire.

### PATRICK BROCKLEBANK

Patrick Brocklebank is the youngest son of a Dublin jeweller. He started his working life as a graphic artist. He writes and paints almost full time, and has had a number of solo and group exhibitions. He holds a Diploma course in print journalism, and joined Dalkey Writers' Workshop in February 2010.

### PHIL LYNCH

Phil Lynch has been writing poetry for many years. His poems have appeared in various magazines and he has read at several 'spoken word' events in Ireland and abroad, including in the Mindfield at the Electric Picnic Festival. Some of his work has been featured on RTE Radio, Balcony TV and Liffey Sound FM.